DROUGHT IN THE UNITED STATES

CAUSES, CONSIDERATIONS AND POLICY RECOMMENDATIONS

ENVIRONMENTAL SCIENCE, ENGINEERING AND TECHNOLOGY

Additional books in this series can be found on Nova's website under the Series tab.

Additional E-books in this series can be found on Nova's website under the E-book tab.

ENVIRONMENTAL SCIENCE, ENGINEERING AND TECHNOLOGY

DROUGHT IN THE UNITED STATES

CAUSES, CONSIDERATIONS AND POLICY RECOMMENDATIONS

JULIE SIMONETTI

AND

MATT SURICKA

EDITORS

New York

For permission to use material from this book please contact us:
Telephone 631-231-7269; Fax 631-231-8175
Web Site: http://www.novapublishers.com

NOTICE TO THE READER

The Publisher has taken reasonable care in the preparation of this book, but makes no expressed or implied warranty of any kind and assumes no responsibility for any errors or omissions. No liability is assumed for incidental or consequential damages in connection with or arising out of information contained in this book. The Publisher shall not be liable for any special, consequential, or exemplary damages resulting, in whole or in part, from the readers' use of, or reliance upon, this material. Any parts of this book based on government reports are so indicated and copyright is claimed for those parts to the extent applicable to compilations of such works.

Independent verification should be sought for any data, advice or recommendations contained in this book. In addition, no responsibility is assumed by the publisher for any injury and/or damage to persons or property arising from any methods, products, instructions, ideas or otherwise contained in this publication.

This publication is designed to provide accurate and authoritative information with regard to the subject matter covered herein. It is sold with the clear understanding that the Publisher is not engaged in rendering legal or any other professional services. If legal or any other expert assistance is required, the services of a competent person should be sought. FROM A DECLARATION OF PARTICIPANTS JOINTLY ADOPTED BY A COMMITTEE OF THE AMERICAN BAR ASSOCIATION AND A COMMITTEE OF PUBLISHERS.

Additional color graphics may be available in the e-book version of this book.

LIBRARY OF CONGRESS CATALOGING-IN-PUBLICATION DATA

ISBN: 978-1-62257-560-2

Published by Nova Science Publishers, Inc. ✝ *New York*

CONTENTS

PREFACE

Drought is a natural hazard with potentially significant societal, economic, and environmental consequences. Public policy issues related to drought range from how to identify and measure drought to how best to prepare for, respond to, and mitigate drought impacts, and who should bear such costs. This book provides information relevant to drought policy discussions by describing the physical causes of drought, drought history in the United States, examples of regional drought conditions, and policy challenges related to drought.

Chapter 1 – Drought is a natural hazard with potentially significant societal, economic, and environmental consequences. Public policy issues related to drought range from how to identify and measure drought to how best to prepare for, respond to, and mitigate drought impacts, and who should bear such costs. This chapter provides information relevant to drought policy discussions by describing the physical causes of drought, drought history in the United States, examples of regional drought conditions, and policy challenges related to drought.

What is drought? Drought is commonly defined as a lack of precipitation over an extended period of time, usually a season or more, relative to some long-term average condition. While the technology and science to predict droughts have improved, regional predictions remain limited to a few months in advance. History suggests that severe and extended droughts are inevitable and part of natural climate cycles.

What causes drought? The physical conditions causing drought in the United States are increasingly understood to be linked to sea surface temperatures (SSTs) in the tropical Pacific Ocean. Studies indicate that cooler-than-average SSTs have been connected to the severe western drought in the first decade of the 21st century, severe droughts of the late 19th century, and precolonial North American "megadroughts." The 2011 severe drought in Texas is thought to be linked to La Niña conditions in the Pacific Ocean.

What is the future of drought in the United States? The prospect of extended droughts and more arid baseline conditions in parts of the United States could suggest new challenges to federal water projects, which were constructed largely on the basis of 20th century climate conditions. Some studies suggest that the American West may be transitioning to a more arid climate, possibly resulting from the buildup of greenhouse gases in the atmosphere, raising concerns that the region may become more prone to extreme drought it was in the 20th century. Some models of future climate conditions also predict greater fluctuations in wet and dry years.

California's 2007-2009 drought exacerbated ongoing tensions among competing water uses. While drought is most common in California and the Southwest, drought also can exacerbate water tensions in other regions. For example, the 2007-2008 drought in the Southeast heightened a long-standing dispute in the Apalachicola-Chattahoochee-Flint River (ACF) basin. Both California and the ACF are again experiencing drought conditions, as are the Rio Grande and Upper Colorado River basins.

What are some drought policy challenges? Although the impacts of drought can be significant nationally as well as regionally, comprehensive national drought policy does not exist. Developing such a policy would represent a significant challenge because of split federal and non-federal responsibilities, the existing patchwork of federal drought programs, and differences in regional conditions and risks. While a comprehensive national policy has not been enacted, Congress has considered and acted upon some of the recommendations issued by the National Drought Policy Commission in 2000. In coming years, Congress may review how federal agencies such as the U.S. Army Corps of Engineers and the Bureau of Reclamation respond to droughts. Congress may also assess other federal programs or choose to reassess the National Drought Policy Commission's recommendations.

Chapter 2 – In July 1998, the 105th Congress enacted Public Law 105-199, the National Drought Policy Act (Appendix A). This law established "an advisory commission to provide advice and recommendations on the creation of an integrated, coordinated Federal policy designed to prepare for and respond to serious drought emergencies." The law directed the Commission to "conduct a thorough study and submit a report on national drought policy."

Commission members were chosen according to provisions in the Act, which required representation of federal and nonfederal government entities and the private sector. The Act directed the current Secretary of the U.S.

Department of Agriculture, Dan Glickman, to chair the Commission. Members of the Commission selected Ronald R. Morriss, County Supervisor of Santa Cruz County, Arizona, and representing the National Association of Counties, as Vice Chair.

This document constitutes the report of the National Drought Policy Commission. The report presents the basis for national drought policy and calls for commitment and resolve in providing sufficient resources to achieve the policy goals.

None of our recommendations should be construed as diminishing the rights of states to control water through state law, as specifically directed by the National Drought Policy Act, nor as interfering in any way with state, local, and tribal sovereignty. All of our recommendations should be considered in light of the need to protect the environment, as also required by the National Drought Policy Act.

In: Drought in the United States   ISBN: 978-1-62257-560-2
Editors: J. Simonetti and M. Suricka   © 2013 Nova Science Publishers, Inc.

Chapter 1

DROUGHT IN THE UNITED STATES: CAUSES AND ISSUES FOR CONGRESS[*]

Peter Folger, Betsy A. Cody and Nicole T. Carter

SUMMARY

Drought is a natural hazard with potentially significant societal, economic, and environmental consequences. Public policy issues related to drought range from how to identify and measure drought to how best to prepare for, respond to, and mitigate drought impacts, and who should bear such costs. This chapter provides information relevant to drought policy discussions by describing the physical causes of drought, drought history in the United States, examples of regional drought conditions, and policy challenges related to drought.

What is drought? Drought is commonly defined as a lack of precipitation over an extended period of time, usually a season or more, relative to some long-term average condition. While the technology and science to predict droughts have improved, regional predictions remain limited to a few months in advance. History suggests that severe and extended droughts are inevitable and part of natural climate cycles.

What causes drought? The physical conditions causing drought in the United States are increasingly understood to be linked to sea surface temperatures (SSTs) in the tropical Pacific Ocean. Studies indicate that cooler-

---

[*] This is an edited, reformatted and augmented version of the Congressional Research Service Publication, CRS Report for Congress RL34580, dated June 12, 2012.

than-average SSTs have been connected to the severe western drought in the first decade of the 21st century, severe droughts of the late 19th century, and precolonial North American "megadroughts." The 2011 severe drought in Texas is thought to be linked to La Niña conditions in the Pacific Ocean.

What is the future of drought in the United States? The prospect of extended droughts and more arid baseline conditions in parts of the United States could suggest new challenges to federal water projects, which were constructed largely on the basis of 20th century climate conditions. Some studies suggest that the American West may be transitioning to a more arid climate, possibly resulting from the buildup of greenhouse gases in the atmosphere, raising concerns that the region may become more prone to extreme drought it was in the 20th century. Some models of future climate conditions also predict greater fluctuations in wet and dry years.

California's 2007-2009 drought exacerbated ongoing tensions among competing water uses. While drought is most common in California and the Southwest, drought also can exacerbate water tensions in other regions. For example, the 2007-2008 drought in the Southeast heightened a long-standing dispute in the Apalachicola-Chattahoochee-Flint River (ACF) basin. Both California and the ACF are again experiencing drought conditions, as are the Rio Grande and Upper Colorado River basins.

What are some drought policy challenges? Although the impacts of drought can be significant nationally as well as regionally, comprehensive national drought policy does not exist. Developing such a policy would represent a significant challenge because of split federal and non-federal responsibilities, the existing patchwork of federal drought programs, and differences in regional conditions and risks. While a comprehensive national policy has not been enacted, Congress has considered and acted upon some of the recommendations issued by the National Drought Policy Commission in 2000. In coming years, Congress may review how federal agencies such as the U.S. Army Corps of Engineers and the Bureau of Reclamation respond to droughts. Congress may also assess other federal programs or choose to reassess the National Drought Policy Commission's recommendations.

INTRODUCTION

The likelihood of extended periods of severe drought, similar to conditions experienced centuries ago, and its effects on 21st century society in the United States raise several issues for Congress. Drought often results in significant agricultural losses, which can have widespread effects. It also can impact other industries and services, including power and energy resource production, navigation, recreation, municipal water supplies, and natural resources such as fisheries and water quality. Addressing drought impacts on an emergency basis is costly to individuals, communities, and businesses. Additionally, hundreds of millions and sometimes billions of dollars in federal assistance can be expended in attempting to manage drought's social consequences.

Drought has afflicted portions of North America for thousands of years. Severe, long-lasting droughts may have been a factor in the disintegration of Pueblo society in the Southwest during the 13th century, and in the demise of central and lower Mississippi Valley societies in the 14th through 16th centuries.[1] In the 20th century, droughts in the 1930s (Dust Bowl era) and 1950s were particularly severe and widespread. In 1934, 65% of the contiguous United States was affected by severe to extreme drought.[2]

Drought conditions are broadly grouped into five categories: (1) abnormally dry, (2) moderate, (3) severe, (4) extreme, and (5) exceptional.[3] Some part of the country is almost always experiencing drought at some level. Since 2000, no less than 7% of the land area of the United States has experienced drought of at least moderate intensity each year.[4] The land area affected by drought of at least moderate intensity varies by year and also within a particular year. For example, since 2000, the total U.S. land area affected by drought of at least moderate intensity has varied from as little as 7% (August 3, 2010) to as much as 46% (September 10, 2002). Based on weekly estimates of the areal extent of drought conditions since 2000, the average amount of land area across the United States affected by at least moderate-intensity drought has been 25%.

While the previous percentages refer to the extent of drought nationally, there is particular concern about those locations experiencing the most intense drought conditions. Nearly every year, *extreme drought*[5] affects some portion of the country. Since 2000, extreme drought or drier conditions have affected approximately 6% of the nation on average.[6] During August 2002, extreme drought extended over 19% of the country. Since 2000, *exceptional drought* conditions have affected approximately 1% of the nation on average. Of particular note were the conditions between June and October 2011; exceptional drought occurred over the largest land area—greater than 9%—during those months, with the affected areas concentrated in Texas.

This chapter discusses how drought is defined (e.g., why drought in one region of the country is different from drought in another region), and why drought occurs in the United States. How droughts are classified, and what is meant by moderate, severe, and extreme drought classifications, are also discussed. The report briefly describes periods of drought in the country's past that equaled or exceeded drought conditions experienced during the 20th century. This is followed by a discussion of the future prospects for a climate in the West that would be drier than the average 20th-century climate. The report concludes with a primer on policy challenges for Congress, such as the existing federal/non-federal split in drought response and management and the patchwork of drought programs subject to oversight by multiple congressional committees. An exhaustive discussion of each policy challenge facing Congress is beyond the scope of this chapter.

WHAT IS DROUGHT?

Drought has a number of definitions; the simplest may be a deficiency of precipitation over an extended period of time, usually a season or more.[7] Drought is usually considered relative to some long-term average condition, or balance, between precipitation, evaporation, and transpiration by plants (evaporation and transpiration are typically combined into one term: evapotranspiration).[8] An imbalance could result from a decrease in precipitation, an increase in evapotranspiration (from drier conditions, higher temperatures, higher winds), or both. It is important to distinguish between drought, which has a beginning and an end, and aridity, which is restricted to low rainfall regions and is a relatively permanent feature of climate (e.g., deserts are regions of relatively permanent aridity).[9]

Higher demand for water for human activities and vegetation in areas of limited water supply increases the severity of drought. For example, drought during the growing season would likely be considered more severe—in terms of its impacts—than similar conditions when cropland lies fallow. For policy purposes, drought often becomes an issue when it results in a water supply deficiency: Less water is available than the average amount for irrigation, municipal and industrial supply (M&I), energy production, preservation of endangered species, and other needs. At the national level, drought is monitored and reported by the National Drought Mitigation Center in an index known as the U.S. Drought Monitor, which synthesizes various drought indices and impacts, and represents a consensus view of ongoing drought conditions between academic and federal scientists.

Drought Is Relative

Drought and "normal" conditions can vary considerably from region to region. For example, in May 2012, the cities of Lubbock, TX, and Athens, GA, were within areas of extreme drought, according to the U.S. Drought Monitor.[10] (See **Figure 1**.) However, extreme drought means something different to Lubbock, in northwest Texas, than it does for Athens, in north central Georgia. Lubbock receives an average total of 3.26 inches of precipitation for the three-month period from February through April of each year.[11] In contrast, Athens receives an average of 12.06 inches over the same time period.[12] From February 2012 through April 2012, Athens received 6.03 inches, which equates to 1.85 times the average precipitation normally received in Lubbock over that time period, but is only 50% of what Athens receives on average. Both cities faced extreme drought compared to normal conditions, but what defines normal for each city differs substantially.

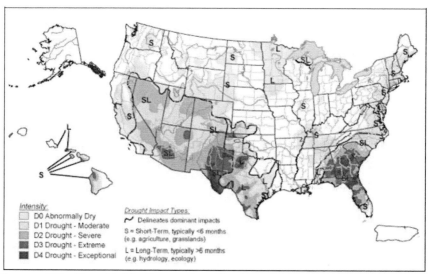

Source: U.S. Drought Monitor, at http://droughtmonitor.unl.edu/, May 8, 2012. Modified by CRS.

Note: The areas delineated on the map as "drought impact types" depict regions where reports of specific impacts (e.g., short term (S) or long term (L) impacts) have been reported and tallied. For more information, see http://www.cpc.ncep.noaa. gov/products/predictions/tools/edb/droughtblends.php.

Figure 1. Extent of Drought in the United States on May 8, 2012.

To deal with these differences, meteorologists use the term meteorological drought—usually defined as the degree of dryness relative to some average amount of dryness and relative to the duration of the dry period. Meteorological drought is region-specific because atmospheric conditions creating precipitation deficiencies vary from region to region, as described above for Lubbock and Athens.

Drought Is Multifaceted

In the past, U.S. Drought Monitor maps have used an "A" to indicate that the primary physical effects are agricultural (crops, pastures, and grasslands) and an "H" to indicate that the primary impacts of drought are hydrological (to water supplies such as rivers, groundwater, and reservoirs). When both effects are apparent, the letters are combined, appearing as "AH." In the newer versions of the maps, such as the one shown in **Figure 1**, the "A" and "H" are replaced with an "S" and "L." These are experimental designations, according to the National Drought Mitigation Center, which produces the U.S. Drought Monitor maps.[13] The "S" designation is intended to indicate a combination of drought indices that reflect impacts that respond to precipitation over several days up to a few months (short-term effects). These would include impact to agriculture, topsoil moisture, unregulated streamflows, and aspects of wildfire danger. The "L" designation approximates responses to precipitation over several months up to a few years (long-term effects). These would include reservoir levels, groundwater, and lake levels. **Figure 1** shows that the region around Lubbock, TX, is designated as L, whereas the region closest to Athens, GA, shows an SL, indicating a combination of short-term and long-term effects.

The U.S. Drought Monitor maps also indicate the intensity of a drought, ranging from abnormally dry (shown as D0 on the maps) to exceptional drought (shown as D4). How these conditions are assessed and how drought is classified are discussed below.

Drought Classification

To assess and classify the intensity and type of drought, certain measures, or drought indices, are typically used. Drought intensity, in turn, is the trigger for local, state, and federal responses that can lead to the flow of billions of dollars in relief to drought-stricken regions.[14] The classification of drought intensity, such as that shown in **Figure 1** for May 8, 2012, may depend on a single indicator or several indicators, often combined with expert opinion from the academic, public, and private sectors. The U.S. Drought Monitor uses five key indicators,[15] together with expert opinion, with indices to account for conditions in the West where snowpack is relatively important, and with other indices used mainly during the growing season.[16] The U.S. Drought Monitor intensity scheme—D0 to D4—is used to depict broad-scale conditions but not necessarily drought circumstances at the local scale. For example, the large regions depicted as red in **Figure 1** faced extreme to exceptional drought conditions in May 2012, but they may contain local areas and individual communities that experienced less (or more) severe drought.[17]

Recent Examples: Texas, California, and Upper Colorado River Basin

Drought in Texas—2011 and 2012

In early May of 2011 over 80% of Texas was experiencing extreme drought, and nearly 50% of the state was in exceptional drought, the most severe level of drought intensity published by the National Drought Mitigation Center.[18] The 2011 drought in Texas represented a dramatic shift compared to the same time period in 2010, when less than 6% of the total land area in Texas was experiencing drought conditions, with no exceptional drought conditions anywhere in the state. (See **Figure 2**, comparing 2010, 2011, and 2012.) In May 2012 the eastern half of Texas had recovered from extreme or exceptional conditions, which—as of May 8, 2012—were affecting 24% and 7% of the state, respectively.

Drought conditions worsened in Texas through the beginning of October 2011, when 88% of the state experienced exceptional drought conditions (and only 3% of the state was not classified as extreme or exceptional drought).[19] Drought conditions generally improved throughout the rest of 2011, but large portions of the state were still affected by extreme or exceptional drought until late winter and early spring of 2012, when the eastern portion of the state recovered to normal or abnormally dry conditions (the least severe category) because of above-normal rainfall from December 2011 through February 2012.[20]

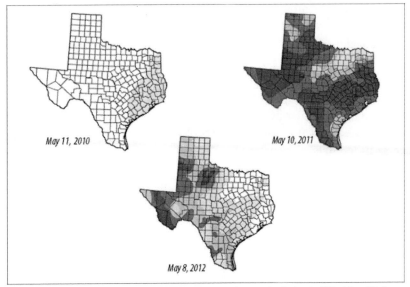

Source: U.S. Drought Monitor, http://droughtmonitor.unl.edu/, Modified by CRS.

Figure 2. Comparison of Drought Conditions in Texas in 2010, 2011, and 2012.

DROUGHT CONDITIONS AFFECTING THE RIO GRANDE PROJECT IN 2011 AND 2012

The 2011 and 2012 drought conditions in Texas and the Southwest have affected the amount of water in the Rio Grande river, which flows south through New Mexico to form the U.S. border between Texas and northern Mexico. The U.S. Bureau of Reclamation's Rio Grande Project, which furnishes irrigation water for approximately 178,000 acres in New Mexico and Texas, as well as electric power, includes the Elephant Butte dam and reservoir and the Caballo Dam and reservoir. Both dams and reservoirs are in New Mexico, and about 60% of the lands receiving irrigation water are in New Mexico. Elephant Butte dam and reservoir provide year-round electric power generation and water during the irrigation season. Water released from Elephant Butte during winter power generation is stored downstream in the Caballo reservoir for irrigation use during the summer. About 40% of the lands receiving water from the project are in Texas, and water is also provided for diversion to Mexico to irrigate about 25,000 acres in the Juarez Valley.

The timing of the water releases in 2012 for delivery to Mexico and their potential impacts on U.S. regional interests (e.g., potential conveyance losses because releases for Mexico would not be timed with deliveries to U.S. water districts) have raised some concerns among some U.S. stakeholders about how scarce regional water resources are to be managed during these dry conditions. Mexican growers sought the surface water deliveries because pumping problems had impaired their ability to start the agricultural season using groundwater.

Inflow to Elephant Butte reservoir in 2011 was less than 15% of the 30-year average for March through July and is expected to be 23% for 2012. The 2011 drought exacerbated low flows into the reservoir; flows into the reservoir have exceeded average runoff values only three times in the past 15 years (1997, 2005, and 2008). As a result, the Elephant Butte reservoir was at 9.6% of the combined reservoir capacity of 2.23 million acre-feet in early September 2011. For April 2012, it was at 17.9% of capacity. Consequently, the average water allocation from the Rio Grande Project in 2011 was approximately 43% (although water available to individual water districts varies). The 2012 allocation is projected to be 20.5%, due to cumulative low inflows in the reservoirs. In contrast, the average allocation in 2009 was 100%.

Due to low water levels, water deliveries from the Rio Grande Project to the irrigation district in Texas (El Paso County Water Improvement District No. 1) as well as to the city of El Paso ended on September 10, 2011. Under a full allocation, the water deliveries normally extend through mid- or late-October. Because of 2011 conditions, the New Mexico portion of the project, operated by the Elephant Butte Irrigation District, stopped taking surface water deliveries in mid-July 2011. Rio Grande Project water users were receiving a 20% allocation of water supplies as of April 1, 2012.

Sources: U.S. Bureau of Reclamation, Rio Grande Project, http://www.usbr.gov/projects/Project.jsp?proj_Name=Rio+Grande+Project; Texas Agrilife Research Center at El Paso, "Drought Watch on the Rio Grande," September 2, 2011, and May 1, 2012; email from Dionne Thompson, Chief, Congressional and Legislative Affairs, U.S. Bureau of Reclamation, September 15, 2011; personal communication with Filiberto Cortez, Division Manager, El Paso Field Office, U.S. Bureau of Reclamation, May 2, 2012; letter from Patrick R. Gordon, Texas Commissioner, Rio Grande Compact Commission, to Edward Drusina, Commissioner, United States Section, International Boundary and Water Commission, April 9, 2012.

According to Texas state climatologist John Nielsen-Gammon, 2011 may be the worst one-year drought on record for Texas.[21] Compounding the effects of abnormally low precipitation, the June-August average temperature in Texas was approximately 2.5 degrees Fahrenheit greater than any previous Texas summer since 1895 and 5 degrees Fahrenheit (F) greater than the long-term average.[22] The 2011 U.S. Drought Monitor showed that Texas had been experiencing both hydrological and agricultural drought, indicating that the drought has caused deficiencies in water supplies as well as deficiencies of water to crops, plants, and grasses.

The most severe Texas drought overall occurred from 1950 to 1957, and had substantial impacts on water supplies across the state because it lasted over many years. Because of the longevity and severity of the 1950s drought, municipal water supplies in Texas today are designed to withstand a drought of similar magnitude, according to the state climatologist.[23] It is difficult to predict whether drought conditions in Texas will persist through 2012 and longer. Long-term precipitation patterns in Texas are influenced by a configuration of sea surface temperatures known as the Pacific Decadal Oscillation (PDO). According to the Texas state climatologist, the current PDO configuration associated with relatively dry weather in Texas has been present since 1998.[24] Similar conditions also prevailed from the 1940s through the 1960s, encompassing the Texas drought of record (1950-1957).

The 2007-2009 California Drought and Outlook for 2012

The 2007-2009 California drought[25] was complicated by decades of tension over water supply deliveries for irrigation and M&I uses, and the preservation of water flows to protect threatened and endangered species. Dry conditions that began in 2007 continued through the 2009 water year (October 2008 through September 2009) and into the fall of 2009. According to the California Department of Water Resources, the 2007-2009 drought was the 12th-driest three-year period in California history since measurements began.[26] Although hydrological conditions were classified as below normal in 2010 and "wet" (well above average) in 2011, the 2012 water year is projected to be "dry" (well below normal).[27] Above-average reservoir storage at the end of 2011 will mitigate reductions to water users; even so, water deliveries to state and federal water project contractors have been restricted for 2012.[28]

During the drought years, drought conditions changed in the state so that some parts of the state experienced more intense drought than others at different times of the year. For example, spring rains reduced the intensity of the drought in some areas—parts of the state classified as extreme in January

2009 were classified as severe in the late spring of that year. Nearly all of California was classified as abnormally dry or under drought conditions through the fall of 2009 until rain and snow in the late fall and early winter of 2010 relieved drought conditions in parts of the state, including the Sierra Nevada. On March 30, 2011, Governor Jerry Brown proclaimed that the drought was over.[29] Most of California remained drought-free from spring 2010 through December 2011—although the winter precipitation in 2011 was abnormally low. The 2012 Drought Monitor shows moderate drought conditions for most of California's Central Valley from January 2012 through April 2012.

California's dry conditions from 2007 through 2009 exacerbated an already tight water supply, where federal and state water deliveries had been reduced in response to a court order to prevent extinction of the Delta smelt.[30] Governor Arnold Schwarzenegger's decision to declare drought in 2008 reflected the meteorological constraints on water supply together with court-imposed restrictions on water supplies to protect endangered species, and long-standing restrictions to protect water quality in the Delta. This combination of factors underscores why drought is complex and not always simply a result of dry conditions.

Similar factors are still in play today. Water deliveries from state and federal water projects for 2012 are restricted due to legal actions to protect threatened and endangered species, water quality requirements, and hydrological factors.

The 2012 Conditions in the Upper Colorado River Basin

Spanning parts of Arizona, California, Colorado, New Mexico, Nevada, Utah, and Wyoming, the Colorado River basin is a critical water supply for the West and portions of northwestern Mexico. Based on inflows observed over the last century, the river is over-allocated, and some contend that supply and demand imbalances are likely to increase in the future.[31] Drought in part of the basin, particularly the upper basin, which is the source of most of the river's flow, exacerbates tensions over the sharing of the resource and results in difficult tradeoffs among the multiple uses of water (e.g., municipal, agricultural, hydropower, energy, recreation, and ecosystem and species demands). How water resources are allocated among these uses within a state is largely determined by state water law, compliance with federal and state laws (including environmental and resource management laws and regulations), and court decisions.

According to the U.S. Drought Monitor, severe drought continued through April 2012 in the Upper Colorado River basin.[32] Although 2011 was a wet water year, upper basin snowpack over the 2011-2012 winter was low,[33] and the snow melted early in the runoff season—one month earlier than normal due to high temperatures in March and April.[34] This early runoff, combined with high reservoir levels carried over from 2011, produced a somewhat paradoxical situation of combined storage in upper basin reservoirs of 127% of average in April 2012,[35] while inflows to the reservoirs are projected to be well below normal. The worries over future conditions are derived from the exceptionally low streamflows projected for the upper basin[36] because of the poor snowpack; low streamflows mean less inflow into reservoirs over the late spring and summer season.[37] Low water availability in the Upper Colorado basin has effects beyond the basin boundaries. For example, Colorado River water is transported from Colorado's Western Slope to the state's Front Range; this water represents a significant contribution to the water available for agricultural and municipal uses in many eastern Colorado counties.

WHAT CAUSES DROUGHT IN THE UNITED STATES?

The immediate cause of drought is:

> the predominant sinking motion of air (subsidence) that results in compressional warming or high pressure, which inhibits cloud formation and results in lower relative humidity and less precipitation. Regions under the influence of semi permanent high pressure during all or a major portion of the year are usually deserts, such as the Sahara and Kalahari deserts of Africa and the Gobi Desert of Asia.[38]

Prolonged droughts occur when these atmospheric conditions persist for months or years over a certain region that typically does not experience such conditions for a prolonged period.[39]

Predicting drought is difficult because the ability to forecast surface temperature and precipitation depends on a number of key variables, such as air-sea interactions, topography, soil moisture, land surface processes, and other weather system dynamics.[40] Scientists seek to understand how all these variables interact and to further the ability to predict sustained and severe droughts beyond a season or two in advance, which is the limit of drought forecasting abilities today.

EL NIÑO-SOUTHERN OSCILLATION (ENSO)

Under normal conditions, the trade winds blow toward the west in the tropical Pacific Ocean, piling up the warm surface waters so that the ocean surface off Indonesia is one-half meter higher than the ocean off Ecuador. As a result, deep and cold water flows up to the surface (upwelling) off the west coast of South America. The upwelling waters are 8 degrees Celsius (14.4 degrees Fahrenheit) cooler than waters in the western Pacific. During El Niño, the trade winds relax, upwelling off South America weakens, and sea surface temperatures rise. The El Niño events occur irregularly at intervals of 2-7 years, and typically last 12-18 months. These events often occur with changes in the Southern Oscillation, a see-saw of atmospheric pressure measured at sea level between the western Pacific and Indian Ocean, and the eastern Pacific. Under normal conditions, atmospheric pressure at sea level is high in the eastern Pacific, and low in the western Pacific and Indian Oceans. As implied by its name, the atmospheric pressure oscillates, or see-saws, between east and west; and during El Niño the atmospheric pressure builds up to abnormally high levels in the western tropical Pacific and Indian Oceans—the El Niño-Southern Oscillation, or ENSO. During a La Niña, the situation is reversed: Abnormally high pressure builds up over the eastern Pacific, the trade winds are abnormally strong, and cooler-than-normal sea surface temperatures occur off tropical South America. Scientists use the terms ENSO or ENSO cycle to include the full range of variability observed, including both El Niño and La Niña events.

Source: Tropical Ocean Atmosphere Project, Pacific Marine Environmental Laboratory, at http://www.pmel.noaa.gov/tao/proj_over/ensodefs.html.

In the tropics, a major portion of the atmospheric variability over months or years seems to be associated with variations in sea surface temperatures (SSTs). Since the mid- to late 1990s, scientists have increasingly linked drought in the United States to SSTs in the tropical Pacific Ocean. Cooler than average SSTs in the eastern tropical Pacific region—"la Niña-like" conditions—have been shown to be correlated with persistently strong drought conditions over parts of the country, particularly the West.[41] A number of recent studies have made the connection between cooler SSTs in the eastern Pacific and the 1998-2004 western drought,[42] three widespread and persistent droughts of the late 19th century,[43] and past North American "megadroughts" that occurred between approximately 900 and 1300 A.D.[44] The precolonial megadroughts apparently lasted longer and were more extreme than any U.S. droughts since 1850, when instrumental records began. Some modeling studies suggest that within a few decades the western United States may again face higher base levels of dryness, or aridity, akin to the 900-1300 A.D. period.[45]

Although the relationship between cooler than normal eastern tropical Pacific SSTs (La Niña-like conditions) and drought is becoming more firmly established, meteorological drought is probably never the result of a single cause. Climate is inherently variable, and accurately predicting drought for one region in the United States for more than a few months or seasons in advance is not yet possible because so many factors influence regional drought. What is emerging from the scientific study of drought is an improved understanding of global linkages—called teleconnections by scientists—between interacting weather systems, such as the El Niño-Southern Oscillation, or ENSO. (See box for a description of ENSO.) For example, some scientists link La Niña conditions between 1998 and 2002 with the occurrence of near-simultaneous drought in the southern United States, Southern Europe, and Southwest Asia.[46]

Prehistorical and Historical Droughts in the United States

Some scientists refer to severe drought as "the greatest recurring natural disaster to strike North America."[47] That claim stems from a reconstruction of drought conditions that extends back over 1,000 years, based on observations, historical and instrumental records where available, and on tree-ring records or other proxies in the absence of direct measurements.[48] What these reconstructions illustrate is that the coterminous United States has experienced periods of severe and long-lasting drought in the western states and also in the more humid East and Mississippi Valley. The drought reconstructions from tree rings document that severe multidecadal drought occurred in the American Southwest during the 13th century, which anthropologists and archeologists suspect profoundly affected Pueblo society. Tree ring drought reconstructions also document severe drought during the 14th, 15th, and 16th centuries in the central and lower Mississippi Valley, possibly contributing to the disintegration of societies in that region.[49]

More recently, a combination of tree ring reconstructions and other proxy data, historical accounts, and some early instrumental records identify three periods of severe drought in the 19th century: 1856-1865 (the "Civil War drought"), 1870-1877, and 1890-1896.[50] The 1856-1865 drought, centered on the Great Plains and Southwest, was the most severe drought to strike the region over the last two centuries, according to one study.[51] The 1890-1896 drought coincided with a period in U.S. history of federal encouragement of large-scale efforts to irrigate the relatively arid western states under authority of the Carey Act.[52] Congressional debate also occurred over a much larger federal role in western states irrigation, which led to the Reclamation Act of 1902.

In the 20th century, the 1930s "Dust Bowl" drought and the 1950s Southwest drought are commonly cited as the two most severe multiyear droughts in the United States.[53] (The 19871989 drought was also widespread and severe, mainly affecting the Great Plains but also instigating extensive western forest fires, including the widespread Yellowstone fire of 1988.) According to several studies, however, the 19th and 20th century severe droughts occurred during a regime of relatively less arid conditions compared to the average aridity in the American West during the 900 to 1300 A.D. megadroughts. One study indicates that the drought record from 900 to 1300 A.D. shows similar variability—drought periods followed by wetter periods— compared to today, but the average climate conditions were much drier and led to more severe droughts.[54]

RESPONDING TO AND PLANNING FOR DROUGHT

Several recent droughts were severe enough to trigger federal responses. When a drought is declared by the U.S. President or by a state governor for a locality or region of the United States, it sets in motion a series of alerts, recommendations, activities, and possible restrictions at the local, regional, or state level, depending on the drought length and severity. Ultimately, a multi-year severe drought could initiate a federal response and transfer of federal dollars to the affected area.

Before drought severity reaches a level triggering a federal response, many states take action. For example, the governor of Alabama issued a drought declaration on March 21, 2008, placing the 10 northernmost counties under an emergency drought declaration level, in accordance with the draft Alabama Drought Management Plan.[55] The emergency drought declaration level for Alabama is its most extreme category of drought. According to Alabama's plan, declaring drought does not "automatically invoke a required response from the various categories of water users;"[56] however, upon confirmation of a drought emergency, the governor's office may issue "public statements that a drought emergency exists, disaster declarations, and the appropriate implementation of water conservation and drought emergency ordinances."[57] The National Drought Mitigation Center posts online copies of drought management, mitigation, or response plans for states and localities, nationwide.[58] The California and Texas governors also have in recent years issued state drought emergency declarations triggering state drought assistance. Some states have also instituted water banks and water transfer mechanisms to deal with water supply shortages (e.g., California, Idaho, and Texas).

Federal Aid

If the effects of a drought overwhelm state or local resources, the President, at the request of the state governor, is authorized under the Stafford Act (42 U.S.C. 5121 et seq.) to issue major disaster or emergency declarations that result in the distribution of federal aid to affected parties.[59] On October 20, 2007, the governor of Georgia requested a presidential drought disaster declaration because of prolonged exceptional drought conditions existing in the northern third of the state.[60] However, no such presidential declaration occurred in response to the request from Georgia. The last presidential drought or water shortage disaster declaration in the continental United States was for New Jersey in 1980. More recent drought declarations have been issued for U.S. territories in the Pacific. More frequently, a state governor requests drought disaster assistance through the U.S. Secretary of Agriculture, who can declare an agricultural disaster as a result of drought and make available low-interest loans and other emergency assistance through various U.S. Department of Agriculture (USDA) programs.[61] For example, on January 4, 2012, USDA designated 40 counties in Texas as primary natural disaster areas due to losses caused by drought, excessive heat, high winds, and wildfires.[62] During the 2011 drought, USDA designated 213 counties in Texas as primary natural disaster areas on June 27, 2011, when 90% of the state was experiencing extreme drought conditions.[63] The U.S. Army Corps of Engineers and the U.S. Bureau of Reclamation also have limited drought emergency authorities and funding (e.g., the Reclamation States Emergency Drought Act, as amended, 43 U.S.C. 2211 et seq.). Under current U.S. farm policy, financial losses caused by drought and other natural disasters are mitigated primarily through the federal crop insurance program (administered by the U.S. Department of Agriculture's Risk Management Agency). From 2000 to 2011, the federal contribution to the crop insurance program averaged about $4.6 billion per year, mostly in the form of a premium subsidy and reimbursements to private insurance companies. Since the severe drought of 1988 and until passage of the 2008 farm bill (P.L. 110-246), Congress regularly made supplemental financial assistance available to farmers and ranchers, primarily in the form of crop disaster payments and emergency livestock assistance. Crop disaster payments, paid to any producer who experienced a major crop loss caused by a natural disaster, totaled $22.34 billion from FY1989 to FY2009. More recently, under the 2008 farm bill (P.L. 110-246), Congress authorized a $3.8 billion trust fund to cover the cost of making agricultural disaster assistance available on an ongoing basis over four years (FY2008-FY2011).[64] Among the authorized programs, the Livestock Forage Disaster Program (LFP) assists ranchers who graze livestock on drought-affected pastureland or grazing land. As of early May 2012, payments under LFP totaled more than $500 million for losses through September 2011.

Federal Facilities and Drought

Even absent federal drought disaster declarations, sustained hydrological drought can affect operations of federally managed reservoirs, dams, locks, hydroelectric facilities, and other components of the nation's water infrastructure. As discussed above, the 2007-2008 Southeast drought directly affected how the Corps manages its facilities in the ACF basin (see box on "Federal Reservoir Operations During Southeast Droughts"). Similarly, drought conditions in California from 2007 to 2009, coupled with declining fish species, resulted in operational changes to Reclamation facilities, including significantly reduced water deliveries to Central Valley Project contractors, as well as to California's State Water Project (SWP) contractors. Reclamation, whose facilities currently serve over 31 million people in the West and deliver a total of nearly 30 million acre-feet of water[65] annually, faces operational challenges because of conflicts among its water users during drought in states it serves.[66] Severe drought conditions in 2001 in the Klamath River basin, on the Oregon-California border, exacerbated competition for scarce water resources among farmers, Indian tribes, commercial and sport fishermen, other recreationists, federal wildlife refuge managers, environmental groups, and state, local, and tribal governments. Reclamation's decision in April 2001 to withhold water from farmers for instream flows for three fish species listed as endangered or threatened under the Endangered

Species Act sparked congressional debate that continues today. The Klamath basin again experienced drought conditions in 2010 and again is experiencing a lower than average water year for 2012. Project water flows to Klamath refuges were halted from December 2011 through March 2012. Dry conditions contributed to a cholera outbreak among migrating birds during this time, resulting in the death of thousands of birds that visit the refuges. However, early spring precipitation improved hydrological conditions such that Reclamation projects full irrigation deliveries for 2012.[68]

FEDERAL RESERVOIR OPERATIONS DURING SOUTHEAST DROUGHTS

An example of hydrological drought was the 2007-2008 drought in the southeastern United States. A persistent severe drought in the region, beginning with below-average rainfall in spring 2006, exacerbated an ongoing interstate dispute involving Alabama, Florida, and Georgia over water sharing in the Apalachicola-Chattahoochee-Flint (ACF) river system. During the drought, Atlanta's municipal and industrial water users in the upper basin were concerned over the potential loss of their principal water supply, Lake Lanier, a surface water reservoir behind a U.S. Army Corps of Engineers operated dam. Their concern resulted from the decision by the Corps to draw down Lake Lanier in the fall of 2007. The Corps drew down the reservoir to maintain minimum flows in the lower basin Apalachicola River to support species protection, energy production (e.g., power plant cooling), and lower basin municipal withdrawals.[67]

The ACF tri-state conflict continues into 2012, and drought conditions have returned to the basin. As of June 2012, the Southeast was experiencing widespread drought, with extreme and exceptional drought in southern Georgia and the northern Florida peninsula. (See **Figure 1**.) Streamflows in the basin in the spring of 2012 were in the lowest quintile on record. Consequently, total inflows into the Corps' ACF reservoirs were below 50% of normal from January to May 2012. As a result, reservoir storage levels are below normal. In May 2012 the Corps shifted its ACF operations to provide only minimum flows to meet water supply, water quality, and environmental needs, thus attempting to store more in its reservoirs. This operation level does not support navigation and only minimal hydropower demands.

During and following the 2007-2008 drought, additional actions at the state level to manage water demand during droughts were used and considered. To what extent similar activities will be implemented or necessary again revives the policy questions of what actions should be taken by whom and when in a shared basin in order to adapt to the dry conditions.

Source: NOAA, National Weather Service, Southeast River Forecast Center, *When Did the Drought Begin, a Focus on the North Georgia and Atlanta Areas*, Nov. 16, 2007; National Integrated Drought Information System, *Southeast US Pilot for Apalachicola-Flint-Chattahoochee River Basin*, June 5, 2012; U.S. Army Corps of Engineers, *Average Daily Inflow to Lakes by Month*, Mobile, AL, June 12, 2012, http://water.sam.usace.army.mil/loclsumm.htm.

The droughts in California, the Southeast, and the Klamath River basin underscore an underlying difficulty of managing federal reservoirs to meet multipurpose water needs. In the future, the United States might face severe and sustained periods of drought not experienced in the 20th century. If so, disputes over federal infrastructure management like those in California, the ACF basin, and Klamath River basin may increasingly determine short-term actions by Reclamation and the Corps, and result in long-term consequences for congressional oversight and funding.

DROUGHT FORECASTS FOR THE UNITED STATES

Predicting the severity and duration of severe drought over a specific region of the country is not yet possible more than a few months in advance because of the many factors that influence drought. Nevertheless, some modeling studies suggest that a transition to a more arid average climate in the American West, perhaps similar to conditions in precolonial North America, may be underway.[69] Some studies have suggested that human influences on climate, caused by emissions of greenhouse gases, may be responsible for a drying trend.[70] Whether future greenhouse gas-driven warming can be linked to La Niña-like conditions, or other phenomena related to the El Niño-Southern Oscillation, is unclear.

A likely consequence of higher temperatures in the West would be higher evapotranspiration, reduced precipitation, and decreased spring runoff.[71] These impacts would result from an "acceleration" of the hydrologic cycle, due to increased warming of the atmosphere, which in turn increases the amount of water held in the atmosphere.[72] A possible consequence is more frequent, and perhaps more severe, droughts and floods. However, these changes are likely not to occur evenly across the United States. Observations of water-related changes over the last century suggest that runoff and streamflow in the Colorado and Columbia River basins has been decreasing, along with the amount of ice in mountain glaciers in the West, and the amount of annual precipitation in the Southwest.[73] Yet the understanding of hydrologic extremes, such as drought, is confounded by other effects such as land cover changes, the operation of dams, irrigation works, extraction of groundwater, and other engineered changes. Forecasting drought conditions at the regional scale, for example for river basins or smaller, is difficult because current climate models are less robust and have higher uncertainty at smaller scales.[74] (For example, see box below on the Colorado River's Lake Mead.)

Even though forecasting drought at the regional scale is difficult, understanding potential changes in long-term trends is important for water managers at all levels—federal, state, local, and tribal. Water project operations and state water allocations are typically based on past long-term hydrological trends; significant deviations from such trends may result in difficult challenges for water managers and water users alike.[75] An example of such a dilemma can be observed in the Colorado River basin.

COLORADO RIVER'S LAKE MEAD

A 2008 study asserted that water storage in Lake Mead has a 50% probability by 2021 to "run dry" and a 10% chance by 2014 to drop below levels needed to provide hydroelectric power under current climate conditions and without changes to water allocation in the basin.

This study raised awareness of the vulnerability of western water systems but drew criticism that global climate models are insufficient to forecast climate change effects at the regional scale. Some western water officials were especially critical of the report's assertions. One explained that Reclamation and other agencies had recently developed new criteria for the allocation of Colorado River water in times of shortages (shortage criteria), including drought, and commented that the likelihood that Lake Mead would run dry was "absurd." The study was based on predictions of future warming in the West without increased precipitation.

In a 2009 follow-up study, the same authors acknowledged that the ability of the Colorado River system to mitigate drought could be managed if the users found a way to reduce average deliveries, thereby maintaining water levels in Lake Mead and Lake Powell at consistently higher elevations. Maintaining higher water levels would increase the capacity of the Colorado River system to buffer itself against low precipitation years. Even so, the authors noted, global climate models are in broad agreement that the southwestern United States is likely to become warmer and more arid, especially in the Colorado River drainage basin. In addition, paleoclimate studies suggest that the 20th century was the wettest or second-wettest century for at least 500 years and possibly over the past 1,200 years. Notwithstanding climate change, the paleoclimate data suggest that average future precipitation in the Colorado River basin is unlikely to match what hydrologists believe were relatively wet 20th-century levels.

Sources: Tim P. Barnett and David W. Pierce, "When Will Lake Mead Go Dry?" *Water Resources Research*, vol. 44 (March 29, 2008), p. W03201, DOI:10.1029/2007WR006704; Felicity Barringer, "Lake Mead could be within a few years of going dry, study finds," *New York Times* (Feb. 13, 2008); Jenny Dennis, "Stunned Scientists: 'When Will Lake Mead Go Dry?'" *Rim Country Gazette* (Feb. 28, 2008), quoting Larry Dozier, Central Arizona Project deputy general manager; Timothy P. Barnett and David W. Pierce, "Sustainable Water Deliveries from the Colorado River in a Changing Climate," *Proceedings of the National Academy of Sciences*, vol. 106, no. 18 (May 6, 2009).

Conditions in the Colorado River basin over the last decade, including recent low reservoir levels in Lake Mead and low flows in the Upper Basin, raise the issue of what is the baseline for average hydrologic cycles now and in the future. The allocation of Colorado River water supplies was agreed upon by lower and upper basin states in the early part of the 20th century based on hydrologic data from what scientists now know was a relatively wet period in the history of the Colorado River basin.[76] If long-term reduced runoff predictions for the basin are borne out (see box above on Colorado River's Lake Mead), then water allocation policies for regions like the Colorado River basin may need to be revisited.[77] In the meantime, Colorado River basin states have negotiated "shortage criteria" and "interim guidelines" for managing Colorado River water supplies during times of shortages.[78]

POLICY CHALLENGES

Severe drought can exacerbate water competition, cause significant economic harm, and affect nearly all areas of the country. Nonetheless, several key factors make comprehensive drought policy at the national level a challenge, including:

- the "creeping" nature of drought;
- split federal and non-federal drought response and management responsibilities;
- a patchwork of federal programs and oversight with little coordination; and
- differences in regional conditions and drought risk in terms of the drought hazard, vulnerability, and potential consequences.

Drought conditions often develop slowly and are not easily identified initially. Consequently, drought declarations are made well after onset—typically once impacts are felt. This situation makes it difficult to mitigate or prevent drought impacts. Further, even though drought generally is continuously occurring somewhere in the United States, the unpredictability of its location, duration, and severity complicates preparation for implementation of responses. When severe meteorological drought affects a region, the supply of available water often shrinks before use is reduced. Adjusting down the use of water as drought persists and supplies shrink can be difficult. Actually, droughts can increase demand on water supplies (e.g., lower soil moisture results in increased demand for irrigation and landscape watering). The flexibility of existing water access and use arrangements limit the scope and speed of some drought responses. Federal, state, and local authorities make water resource decisions within the context of multiple and often conflicting laws and objectives, competing legal decisions, and entrenched institutional mechanisms, including century-old water rights and long-standing contractual obligations (i.e., long-term water delivery and power contracts). Typically, how access to and competition for water is managed (e.g., permitting of water withdrawals) and how reductions in water supply are managed (e.g., shared reductions under a riparian system of water rights versus reductions based on the priority in time of a water right) is determined by state law and at times through interstate compacts. Additionally, state and local laws can determine how easily water can be transferred among users. These access, reduction, and transfer arrangements can significantly affect the behavior, incentives, and opportunities available to water users during droughts. Fundamental changes to the access, reduction, and transfer arrangements are largely outside of the realm of federal action, and are largely determined by each state.

AUSTRALIA'S DROUGHT EXPERIENCE: WATER MARKETS AS DROUGHT MANAGEMENT

Australia experienced a historic drought from 1997 to 2009, known as the Millennium Drought. The drought tested a preexisting multi-pronged national water reform initiative; one aspect of the reform was the development of water markets. To develop water markets, the initiative had promoted reform of state law to clarify the property right associated with a water right and facilitated the means to buy and sell perpetual water rights and short-term allocations in basins that were fully allocated. Water trade increased significantly during the later years of the drought as allocations fell and markets matured. Allocations in some sub-basins during the worst of the drought reached as low as 20% of a full allocation. While gross domestic production dropped by $2 billion-$3 billion in Australia's most significant agricultural basin during each of the worst drought years, the ability to trade water is estimated to have reduced losses by roughly $1 billion during each drought year. The market's ability to move scarce water to uses with higher economic value is credited with assisting Australia's rural economy to ride out the drought as well as it did by getting more value per unit of water used. For example, some dairy farmers sold their water rights and purchased fodder, rather than growing it themselves.

Agricultural businesses increasingly used buying and selling in the water market as a coping mechanism as the drought persisted. With water availability high in many basins since 2009, market water prices have fallen, and rice and cotton production, which had declined during the drought, have picked back up.

Water markets were not established in Australia without controversy and criticism. While not solely responsible, water rights trading contributed to trends producing significant economic adjustment, particularly in rural agricultural communities. Nonetheless, contemplating the consequences for Australia, especially its agricultural communities and businesses, of such a severe drought under a less flexible water rights regime has increased internal support for the use and further improvement of water markets.

The broader water reform initiative produced some disappointments, as well as successes. The broader reform is criticized for falling short of achieving ecologically sustainable levels of surface water withdrawals. Consequently, the recent discourse about the next steps in Australian water policy has focused on how to establish sustainable levels of withdrawals that can maintain ecosystems and support regional economies and how to cost-effectively secure the water for the environment. Australia's government uses the water markets to transition water out of existing uses for use in meeting environmental flow goals; to date, the Australian government's purchase of water rights for the environment using the market has been less expensive than obtaining the water through infrastructure efficiency improvements.

Source: National Water Commission (Australia), *The Impacts of Water Trading in the Southern Murray-Darling Basin Between 2006-07 and 2010-11*, April 2012.

A mismatch between supply and demand during droughts underscores the responsibility of stakeholders to anticipate the influence of drought and plan and act accordingly. The federal government has several drought monitoring and response programs. While drought planning and mitigation responsibilities lie largely at the state and local level, the federal government also provides some drought planning assistance. Additionally, the federal government often provides emergency funding for drought relief that is primarily aimed at easing the economic impacts. The National Drought Commission and others have noted, however, that federal relief programs and emergency funding provide little incentive for state and local planning and drought mitigation. A policy issue particularly relevant to state and local decision makers is the role and types of demand management tools to employ during a drought (e.g., lawn watering restrictions, incentives to curtail irrigation during droughts, scarcity pricing). How a state distributes and administers its waters among competing uses can affect what drought response tools are available to it and to water users.

A further challenge is lack of a cohesive national drought policy at the federal level, and lack of a lead agency coordinating federal programs. Rather, several federal programs have been developed over the years, often in response to specific droughts. Additionally, occasional widespread economic effects have prompted creation of several federal relief programs. These programs are overseen by different congressional committees. Whether this fragmentation results in duplication, waste, and gaps, or whether it reflects the complexity of preparing and responding to drought and the different responses needed by a wide range of stakeholders (e.g., irrigated agriculture, dry land farming, municipal water utilities) is part of the debate about how to proceed with cost-effective management of the nation's drought risk and who bears the consequences of drought. (See box above for an example of how water access and transfer arrangements played a significant role in shaping Australia's drought resilience and adaptation.)

Legislative Action

Congress has long recognized the lack of coordinated drought planning and mitigation activities among federal agencies and the predominance of a crisis management approach to dealing with drought. Over the last 15 years, legislative action has focused on the question of whether there is a need for a national drought policy. For example, in 1998, Congress passed the National Drought Policy Act (P.L. 105-199), which created a National Drought Policy Commission. In 2000, the commission submitted to Congress a comprehensive report that included policy recommendations. Congress has considered recommendations from the commission's 2000 report; however, to date, it has enacted only one part of the recommendations (the National Integrated Drought Information System, discussed below). Congress also considered, but did not enact, legislation creating a National Drought Council during deliberations on the 2008 farm bill. Both the commission findings and the proposed council are discussed below.

The National Drought Policy Act of 1998

In passing the National Drought Policy Act of 1998, Congress found that "at the Federal level, even though historically there have been frequent, significant droughts of national consequences, drought is addressed mainly through special legislation and ad hoc action rather than through a systematic and permanent process as occurs with other natural disasters."[79] Further, Congress found an increasing need at the federal level to emphasize preparedness, mitigation, and risk management. Those findings are consistent with a recognition of the inevitability, albeit unpredictability, of severe drought occurring.

The act created the National Drought Policy Commission, and required the commission to conduct a study and submit a report to Congress on:

- what is needed to respond to drought emergencies;
- what federal laws and programs address drought;
- what are the pertinent state, tribal, and local laws; and
- how various needs, laws, and programs can be better integrated while recognizing the primacy of states to control water through state law.

In May 2000, the commission submitted its report,[80] which included 29 specific recommendations to achieve the goals of national drought policy, including the establishment of a National Drought Council. (The **Appendix** of this chapter lists the five goals in the commission's report.) As background for its recommendations, the commission noted the patchwork nature of drought programs, and that despite a major federal role in responding to drought, no single federal agency leads or coordinates drought programs—instead, the federal role is more of "crisis management."[81] Most of the specific recommendations were targeted at the President and federal agencies, coupled with calls for Congress to fund drought-related activities in support of the recommendations. An overarching recommendation was for Congress to pass a National Drought Preparedness Act to implement the commission's recommendations.

National Drought Preparedness Legislation and the 2008 Farm Bill

National Drought Preparedness Act bills were introduced in 2002 (107th Congress), 2003 (108th Congress), and 2005 (109th Congress), but were not enacted. Similar stand-alone legislation was introduced in the 110th Congress; however, the House-passed version of H.R. 2419, the Farm, Nutrition, and Bioenergy Act of 2008 (also known as the 2008 farm bill), contained a section creating a National Drought Council. This section of the 2008 farm bill would have charged the council with creating a national drought policy action plan, which would have incorporated many of the components recommended in the commission's report; however, it was not included in the conference agreement. Although the Senate version of H.R. 2419 did not contain a similar section, the Senate bill authorized permanent disaster payments in hopes of precluding the need for ad hoc disaster payments. The conference agreement on the 2008 farm bill (P.L. 110-246, enacted June 18, 2008) included a new $3.8 billion trust fund to cover the cost of making agricultural disaster assistance available on an ongoing basis over the following four years. The assistance was available for disasters occurring on or before September 30, 2011, and has since expired. The Senate Agriculture Committee version of the

2012 farm bill would authorize four of the five disaster programs that received funding under the authority of the 2008 farm bill.[82]

National Integrated Drought Information System

Although Congress has not enacted comprehensive national drought preparedness legislation, it acted on the second of five commission goals by passing the National Integrated Drought Information System (NIDIS) Act of 2006 (P.L. 109-430). That goal called for enhanced observation networks, monitoring, prediction, and information delivery of drought information. P.L. 109-430 established NIDIS within the National Oceanic and Atmospheric Administration (NOAA) to improve drought monitoring and forecasting abilities.[83]

CONCLUSION

Drought is a natural hazard with potentially significant economic, social, and ecological consequences. History suggests that severe and extended droughts are inevitable and part of natural climate cycles. Drought has for centuries shaped the societies of North America and will continue to do so into the future. Current understanding is that the physical conditions causing drought in the United States are linked to sea surface temperatures in the tropical Pacific Ocean. For example, the 2011 severe drought in Texas is thought to be linked to La Niña conditions in the Pacific Ocean. Increasingly, studies are projecting the long-term role that droughts may play in regional climate patterns. Nonetheless, available technology and science remains limited to forecasting specific drought beyond a few months in advance for a region. The prospect of extended droughts and more arid baseline conditions in parts of the United States represents a challenge to existing public policy responses for preparing and responding to drought, and to federal water resource projects in particular, because their construction was based largely on 19th-and 20th-century hydrologic conditions.

Over time, Congress has created various drought programs, often in response to specific droughts and authored by different committees. Crafting a broad drought policy that might encompass the jurisdiction of many different congressional committees is often difficult. Additionally, although many water allocation and other water management responsibilities largely lie at the state or local level, localities and individuals often look to the federal government for relief when disasters occur. This is similar to the situation for flood policy, and water policy in general, at the national level. The National Drought Policy Commission recognized these patterns, and they underlie many of its recommendations to Congress.[84] The currently fragmented approach can be costly to national taxpayers; however, it is not certain that increased federal investment (especially vis-à-vis the potential for tailored local and state investment) in drought preparation, mitigation, and improved coordination would produce more economically efficient outcomes.

The overall costs to the federal government as a result of extreme drought, apart from relief to the agricultural sector, are difficult to assess. As discussed above, the operation of the nation's complex federal water infrastructure is affected by drought.

Congress may opt to revisit the commission's recommendations and reevaluate whether current federal practices could be supplemented with actions to coordinate, prepare for, and respond to the unpredictable but inevitable occurrence of drought. Given the daunting task of managing drought, Congress also may consider proposals to manage drought impacts, such as assisting localities, industries, and agriculture with developing or augmenting water supplies. Congress also may move to examine how the two major federal water management agencies, the Corps and Reclamation, plan for and respond to severe drought and account for its impacts.

APPENDIX. EXCERPT FROM THE 2000 NATIONAL DROUGHT POLICY COMMISSION REPORT TO CONGRESS

The following is an excerpt from the 2000 National Drought Policy Commission Report to Congress: *Preparing for Drought in the 21st Century— A Report of the National Drought Policy Commission.*

Policy Statement

- Favor preparedness over insurance, insurance over relief, and incentives over regulation.
- Set research priorities based on the potential of the research results to reduce drought impacts.
- Coordinate the delivery of federal services through cooperation and collaboration with nonfederal entities.

Goals

Goal 1. Incorporate planning, implementation of plans and proactive mitigation measures, risk management, resource stewardship, environmental considerations, and public education as the key elements of effective national drought policy.

Goal 2. Improve collaboration among scientists and managers to enhance the effectiveness of observation networks, monitoring, prediction, information delivery, and applied research and to foster public understanding of and preparedness for drought.

Goal 3. Develop and incorporate comprehensive insurance and financial strategies into drought preparedness plans.

Goal 4. Maintain a safety net of emergency relief that emphasizes sound stewardship of natural resources and self-help.

Goal 5. Coordinate drought programs and response effectively, efficiently, and in a customer-oriented manner.

End Notes

[1] Edward R. Cook, Richard Seager, Mark A. Crane, and David W. Stahle, "North American drought: reconstructions, causes, and consequences," *Earth-Science Reviews*, vol. 81 (2007): pp. 93-134. Hereafter referred to as Cook et al., 2007.

[2] Donald A. Wilhite, et al., *Managing Drought: A Roadmap for Change in the United States* (Boulder, CO: The Geological Society of America, 2007), p. 12; at http://www.geosociety. org/meetings/06drought/roadmap.pdf.

[3] These are the categories used by the National Drought Mitigation Center (NDMC). The NDMC helps prepare the U.S. Drought Monitor and maintains its website.

[4] NDMC data collected since 2000. U.S. Drought Monitor at the NDMC in Lincoln, NE. See http://droughtmonitor.unl.edu/dmtabs_archive.htm.

[5] Extreme drought is the fourth of five categories indicating drought conditions, ranging from abnormally dry to exceptional drought, according to the National Drought Mitigation Center.

[6] In some years or months, however, no part of the country was under extreme or exceptional drought. For example, from January 2000 through early April 2000, extreme or exceptional drought did not affect any portion of the country.

[7] NDMC, http://www.drought.unl.edu/DroughtBasics/WhatisDrought.aspx.

[8] Evapotranspiration may be defined as the loss of water from a land area through transpiration from plants and evaporation from the soil and surface water bodies such as lakes, ponds, and manmade reservoirs.

[9] Permanently arid conditions reflect the *climate* of the region, which is the composite of the day-to-day weather over a longer period of time. Climatologists traditionally interpret climate as the 30-year average. See NDMC, http://www.drought.unl.edu/DroughtBasics/Whatis Climatology.aspx.

[10] See U.S. Drought Monitor, http://www.drought.unl.edu/dm/monitor.html.

[11] The National Weather Service Forecast Office, Lubbock, Texas, http://www.weather.gov/climate/index.php?wfo=lub.

[12] The National Weather Service Forecast Office, Peachtree City, GA, http://www.nws.noaa.gov/climate/index.php?wfo=ffc.

[13] The complete designations are referred to as experimental objective blends of drought indicators, http://www.cpc.ncep.noaa.gov/products/predictions/tools/edb/droughtblends.php.

[14] For example, the Palmer Drought Index has been widely used by the U.S. Department of Agriculture to determine when to grant emergency drought assistance. See NDMC, http://drought.unl.edu/Planning/Monitoring/ComparisonofIndicesIntro/PDSI.aspx.

[15] The five key indicators include the Palmer Drought Index, the Climate Prediction Center soil moisture model, U.S. Geological Survey weekly streamflow data, the Standardized Precipitation Index, and short- and long-term drought indicator blends. For a discussion of drought indices, see NDMC, http://droughtmonitor.unl.edu/current.html.

[16] U.S. Drought Monitor, http://www.drought.unl.edu/dm/classify.htm.

[17] The "S" and "L" terms shown in **Figure 1** give additional information on the nature of the drought in the affected region. For more information on the reasoning behind the classification schemes, see http://droughtmonitor.unl.edu/classify.htm.

[18] U.S. Drought Monitor, http://droughtmonitor.unl.edu/dmtabs_archive.htm.

[19] See the U.S. Drought Monitor, Texas, on October 4, 2011, http://droughtmonitor.unl.edu/archive.html.

[20] "Climate Abyss: Weather and Climate Issues with John Nielsen-Gammon," *Texas Drought Update*, March 23, 2012, http://blog.chron.com/climateabyss/2012/03/texas-drought-update/.

[21] Office of the Texas State Climatologist, "Texas Drought Officially the Worst Ever," August 4, 2011, http://tamunews.tamu.edu/2011/08/04/texas-drought-officially-the-worst-ever/.

[22] John W. Nielsen-Gammon, *The 2011 Texas Drought: A Briefing Packet for the Texas Legislature*, October 31, 2011, p. 29, http://climatexas.tamu.edu/files/2011_drought.pdf.

[23] Office of the Texas State Climatologist, "Texas Drought Officially the Worst Ever," August 4, 2011, http://tamunews.tamu.edu/2011/08/04/texas-drought-officially-the-worst-ever/.

[24] John W. Nielsen-Gammon, The *2011 Texas Drought: A Briefing Packet for the Texas Legislature*, p. 41.

[25] For more information about the hydrology and policy issues involved in the 2007-2009 California drought, see CRS Report R40079, *California Drought: Hydrological and Regulatory Water Supply Issues*, by Betsy A. Cody, Peter Folger, and Cynthia Brougher.

[26] California Department of Water Resources, *California's Drought of 2007-2009—An Overview*, September 2010, http://www.water.ca.gov/waterconditions/drought/docs/DroughtReport2010.pdf.

[27] For information on water year classifications and water allocations to federal water contractors in California, see http://www.usbr.gov/mp/PA/water/.

[28] Ibid.

[29] Office of Governor Edmund G. Brown, Jr., "A Proclamation by the Governor of the State of California—Drought," http://gov.ca.gov/news.php?id=16997.

[30] The Delta smelt is a species of fish. *Natural Resources Defense Council v. Kempthorne*, No. 1:05-cv-1207 OWWGSA (E.D. Cal., December 14, 2007).

[31] Bureau of Reclamation, U.S. Department of the Interior, *Colorado River Basin Water Supply and Demand Study, Phase 4: Development and Evaluation of Opportunities for Balancing Water Supply and Demand*, November 2011, http://www.usbr.gov/lc/region/programs/crbstudy/OptionsSubmittalReport.pdf.

[32] National Weather Service, *Drought Information Statement—Denver/Boulder*, CO, May 3, 2012, http://www.srh.noaa.gov/productview.php?pil=DGTBOU.

[33] Natural Resources Conservation Service, U.S. Department of Agriculture, *Westwide Snotel Current Snow Water Equivalent (SWE) % of Normal*, May 1, 2012, http://ccc.atmos. colostate.edu/pdfs/NIDIS_01_May_2012.pdf.

[34] Letter from Water Resources Group, Bureau of Reclamation to All Colorado River Annual Operation Plan (AOP) Recipients, April 24-Month Study, April 10, 2012, http://www.usbr. gov/uc/water/crsp/studies/24Month_04.pdf. Hereafter Water Resources Group, April 10, 2012.

[35] Ibid. High inflows in spring and summer of 2011 improved storage levels at basin reservoirs; for instance, Lake Powell increased its storage from 53% in 2010 to 64% in 2011.

[36] Natural Resources Conservation Service, U.S. Department of Agriculture, *Spring and Summer Streamflow Forecasts as of May 1, 2012*, http://www.wcc.nrcs.usda.gov/ftpref/support/ water/westwide/streamflow/wy2012/strm1205.gif.

[37] Water Resources Group, April 10, 2012.

[38] See NDMC, at http://drought.unl.edu/DroughtBasics/PredictingDrought.aspx.

[39] Ibid.

[40] Ibid.

[41] Cook et al., 2007.

[42] Hoerling, Martin and Arun Kumar, "The perfect ocean for drought," Science, vol. 299 (January 31, 2003), pp. 691-694. Hereafter referred to as Hoerling and Kumar, 2003.

[43] Herweiger, Celine, Richard Seager, and Edward Cook, "North American droughts of the mid to late nineteenth century: a history, simulation and implication for Mediaeval drought," The Holocene, vol. 15, no. 2 (January 31, 2006),pp. 159-171. Hereafter referred to as Herweiger et al., 2006.

[44] Cook et al., 2007.

[45] Richard Seager et al., "Model projections of an imminent transition to a more arid climate in southwestern North America," *Science*, vol. 316 (May 25, 2007): pp. 1181-1184.

[46] Hoerling and Kumar, 2003.

[47] Cook et al., 2007.

[48] Proxies are indirect measurements typically used where direct measurements are unavailable. Tree rings can be used as a proxy for measuring dryness and drought. Similarly, ice cores from glaciers and polar caps can be used as proxies for measuring atmospheric temperatures and carbon dioxide concentrations from thousands of years ago.

[49] Cook et al., 2007.

[50] Herweiger et al., 2006.

[51] Ibid.

[52] The Carey Act, signed into law on August 18, 1894 (Chapter 301, Section 4, 28 Stat. 422), initially made available up to 1 million acres of federal land in each state, provided that the state met several requirements for the eventual development of water resources for reclamation. Some observers have suggested that the failure of the Carey Act to foster irrigation projects in all the land made available, compounded in part by the 1890-1896 drought, led to the Reclamation Act of 1902 and the emergence of the Bureau of Reclamation in the 20th century. (See Marc Reisner, *Cadillac Desert* (New York, New York, Penguin Books, 1986)).

[53] Fye, F., D.W. Stahle, and E.R. Cook, "Paleoclimate analogs to twentieth century moisture regimes across the United States," *Bulletin of the American Meteorological Society*, 2003, vol. 84, pp. 901-909.

[54] For example, one report showed that 42% of the area studied in the American West was affected by drought during the years 900 to 1300, versus 30% between 1900 and 2003, a 29% reduction in the average area affected by drought between the two periods. See Cook et al., 2007.

[55] For more information, see http://www.adeca.alabama.gov/Office%20of%20Water%20 Resources/Document%20Library/20080321%20-%20DroughtAdvisoryMap_Final.pdf.

[56] Alabama Drought Management Plan, p. 7.

[57] Ibid., p. 8.

[58] For more information, see http://drought.unl.edu/Planning/PlanningInfobyState.aspx.

[59] For more information about the Stafford Act, see CRS Report RL33053, *Federal Stafford Act Disaster Assistance: Presidential Declarations, Eligible Activities, and Funding*, by Francis X. McCarthy; and CRS Report R41981, *Congressional Primer on Major Disasters and Emergencies*, by Francis X. McCarthy and Jared T. Brown.

[60] See http://www.fema.gov/news/disasters.fema.

[61] For more information, see CRS Report RS21212, *Agricultural Disaster Assistance*, by Dennis A. Shields and Ralph M. Chite. See also CRS Report RL34207, *Crop Insurance and Disaster Assistance in the 2008 Farm Bill*, by Ralph M. Chite and Dennis A. Shields.

[62] U.S. Department of Agriculture, Farm Service Agency News Release, January 4, 2012, http://www.fsa.usda.gov/FSA/newsReleases?area=newsroom&subject=landing&topic=edn&newstype=ednewsrel&type=detail&item=ed_20120104_rel_0003.html.

[63] U.S. Department of Agriculture, Farm Service Agency News Release, June 27, 2011, http://www.fsa.usda.gov/FSA/newsReleases?area=newsroom&subject=landing&topic=edn&newstype=ednewsrel&type=detail&item=ed_20110628_rel_0061.html.

[64] The causes of crop loss can vary dramatically from year to year, although drought is one of the most common, if not the most common, cause of crop loss. See CRS Report RS21212, *Agricultural Disaster Assistance*, by Dennis A. Shields and Ralph M. Chite, and CRS Report RL31095, *Emergency Funding for Agriculture: A Brief History of Supplemental Appropriations, FY1989-FY2012*, by Ralph M. Chite for more information.

[65] One acre-foot is enough water to cover one acre of land one foot deep. An acre-foot is equivalent to 325,851 gallons. For more information about federal water supply programs, see CRS Report RL30478, *Federally Supported Water Supply and Wastewater Treatment Programs*, coordinated by Claudia Copeland and others.

[66] Reclamation is a central player in water resource management in the West, and a devastating drought at the end of the 19th century was probably one of the many factors that led to the 1902 Reclamation Act that launched the federal reclamation effort and Reclamation itself. See Marc Reisner, *Cadillac Desert* (New York: Penguin, 1986), pp. 108-109. Other research suggests that the failures of some late 19th century private irrigation projects, undertaken following passage of the Carey Act (see footnote 52), may have occurred in part due to drought conditions.

[67] For more information on the ACF 2007-2008 drought and tri-state conflict, see CRS Report RL34326, *Apalachicola-Chattahoochee-Flint (ACF) Drought: Federal Water Management Issues*, coordinated by Nicole T. Carter; and CRS Report RL34440, *Apalachicola-Chattahoochee-Flint Drought: Species and Ecosystem Management*, by M. Lynne Corn, Kristina Alexander, and Eugene H. Buck.

[68] U.S. Bureau of Reclamation, *Klamath Project 2012 Operations Plan*, April 6, 2012, p. 5, http://www.usbr.gov/mp/kbao/docs/summer_operations.pdf.

[69] Richard Seager et al., "Model projections of an imminent transition to a more arid climate in southwestern North America," *Science*, vol. 316 (May 25, 2007), pp. 1181-1184.

[70] Tim P. Barnett, et al., "Human-induced changes in the hydrology of the western United States," *Science*, vol. 319 (February 22, 2008), pp. 1080-1082.

[71] Research results are emerging, however, that suggest that local and regional patterns of precipitation may be variable, and parts of a region or a state could receive higher precipitation than the current average, even if the overall trend over the broader area is towards less precipitation. See K. T. Redmond, "Climate Change in the Western United States: Projections and Observations," *Eos Trans. AGU*, 90(52), Fall Meet. Suppl., Abstract U11D-02, 2009.

[72] National Research Council, Committee on Hydrologic Science, *Global Change and Extreme Hydrology: Testing Conventional Wisdom*, Washington, D.C., 2011, p. 3.

[73] Ibid., p. 7.

[74] Ibid., p. 9.

[75] P.C.D. Milly et al., "Stationarity Is Dead: Whither Water Management?," *Science*, vol. 319 (February 4, 2008), p. 574.

[76] The Colorado River basin is somewhat unusual in that the Secretary of the Interior acts as water "master" for the river, and apportionment of water supplies among the basin states is done in accordance with the Colorado River Compact and a body of law known as the "Law of the River." For more information on the Law of the River, see http://www.usbr.gov/lc/region/g1000/lawofrvr.html.

[77] Tim P. Barnett and David W. Pierce, "When Will Lake Mead Go Dry?" Water Resources Research, vol. 44 (March 29, 2008), p. W03201, DOI: 10.1029/2007WR006704. Reservoir storage in the Colorado River basin has increased by more than 8 million acre-feet since 2005. As of April 3, 2012, reservoir storage in the basin was nearly 63% of capacity. Hydropower production has continued under 2007 "interim guidelines" for managing water shortages in the Lower Colorado River basin.

[78] For more information on 2012 operations, see http://www.usbr.gov/uc/water/crsp/studies/24Month_03.pdf, accessed May 2, 2012. CRS has not determined to what degree recent scenarios are similar to those considered in studies supporting the new shortage criteria for Colorado River water allocations under the Colorado River Compact.

[79] The National Drought Policy Act of 1998, P.L. 105-199 (42 U.S.C. 5121 note).

[80] Available at http://govinfo.library.unt.edu/drought/finalreport/fullreport/ndpcfullreportcovers/ndpcreportcontents.htm.

[81] Ibid., p. 1.

[82] See CRS Report R42040, *Farm Safety Net Proposals in the 112th Congress*, by Dennis A. Shields and Randy Schnepf.

[83] NOAA allocated $12.1 million for NIDIS in FY2012. For more information about NIDIS, see http://www.drought.gov.

[84] *Infra*, note 52.

In: Drought in the United States   ISBN: 978-1-62257-560-2
Editors: J. Simonetti and M. Suricka   © 2013 Nova Science Publishers, Inc.

Chapter 2

PREPARING FOR DROUGHT IN THE 21ST CENTURY[*]

National Drought Policy Commission

FOREWORD

In July 1998, the 105th Congress enacted Public Law 105-199, the National Drought Policy Act (Appendix A). This law established "an advisory commission to provide advice and recommendations on the creation of an integrated, coordinated Federal policy designed to prepare for and respond to serious drought emergencies." The law directed the Commission to "conduct a thorough study and submit a report on national drought policy."

Commission members were chosen according to provisions in the Act, which required representation of federal and nonfederal government entities and the private sector. The Act directed the current Secretary of the U.S. Department of Agriculture, Dan Glickman, to chair the Commission. Members of the Commission selected Ronald R. Morriss, County Supervisor of Santa Cruz County, Arizona, and representing the National Association of Counties, as Vice Chair.

This document constitutes the report of the National Drought Policy Commission. The report presents the basis for national drought policy and

---

[*] This is an edited, reformatted and augmented version of the U.S. Department of Agriculture's Office of Communications (Design and Printing Center) and the National Drought Policy Commission staff.

calls for commitment and resolve in providing sufficient resources to achieve the policy goals.

None of our recommendations should be construed as diminishing the rights of states to control water through state law, as specifically directed by the National Drought Policy Act, nor as interfering in any way with state, local, and tribal sovereignty. All of our recommendations should be considered in light of the need to protect the environment, as also required by the National Drought Policy Act.

SUMMARY

Drought will occur at some time every year in the United States. It can and does extend over long periods and large areas, and it brings hardship.

Each time drought occurs, many of the same issues are raised. Principally, how much damage was inflicted, on whom, and where? Who is going to pay for it? How can we prevent or at least reduce damages and their costs in the future?

In 1998, Congress passed the National Drought Policy Act. The Act stated that this nation would benefit from national drought policy based on preparedness and mitigation to reduce the need for emergency relief. It acknowledged that this country has no consistent, comprehensive policy driving the federal role to help reduce the impacts of drought. The Act also created the National Drought Policy Commission to advise Congress on how best to:

- Integrate federal drought laws and programs with ongoing state, local, and tribal programs into a comprehensive national policy to mitigate the impacts of and respond to drought.
- Improve public awareness of the need for drought mitigation.
- Achieve a coordinated approach to drought mitigation and response by governments and nongovernmental entities, including academic, private, and nonprofit interests.

The Commission contends that we can reduce this nation's vulnerability to the impacts of drought by making preparedness—especially drought planning, plan implementation, and proactive mitigation—the cornerstone of national drought policy.

Policy Statement

The Commission believes that national drought policy should use the resources of the federal government to support but not supplant nor interfere with state, tribal, regional, local, and individual efforts to reduce drought impacts. The guiding principles of national drought policy should be:

1. Favor preparedness over insurance, insurance over relief, and incentives over regulation.
2. Set research priorities based on the potential of the research results to reduce drought impacts.
3. Coordinate the delivery of federal services through cooperation and collaboration with nonfederal entities.

This policy requires a shift from the current emphasis on drought relief. It means we must adopt a forward-looking stance to reduce this nation's vulnerability to the impacts of drought. Preparedness—especially drought planning, plan implementation, and proactive mitigation—must become the cornerstone of national drought policy. This basic concept was the conclusion reached by the Senate Task Force on Funding Disaster Relief in March 1995, among other entities. It was universally supported within the Commission and by the overwhelming majority of people who commented on the draft version of this chapter.

Basis of Recommendations

The Commission's recommendations are based on our findings about the gaps among what is needed and what is provided by state, regional, local, tribal, and federal drought programs and laws. The findings stem from information presented by witnesses at our public hearings across the country and in written comments submitted independently, as well as from our own experience.

In keeping with the law that established the Commission, our recommendations relate primarily to the federal government's role in national drought policy. We view the federal government as one of many partners needed to reduce the impacts of drought. Much of the work must be accomplished by state, local, and tribal governments and regional entities such as river basin planning commissions and water districts. As our recommendations attest, federal resources should be used to augment the vital drought-related programs of these other entities.

    In identifying drought as the top weather event of the 20th century, the climate periodical Weatherwise (November/December 1999) had this to say: "More than any other weather or climate event, the 1930s drought shaped American society. The Dust Bowl caused a legendary and influential migration from the Southern Plains to California, revolutionized agricultural policy on the Plains, and synchronized with the Great Depression to compound that event's misery for millions. Even now, hundreds of heat records from the 1930s still stand across the Plains, and no drought this century attacked so much of the country for so long. At its height in July 1934, nearly two-thirds of the nation was considered to be in a severe to extreme drought."

Summary of Recommendations

    We recommend first that Congress pass a National Drought Preparedness Act to establish a nonfederal/federal partnership through a National Drought Council as described in Recommendation 5.1 in the recommendations section of this chapter. The primary function of the Council is to ensure that the goals of national drought policy are achieved. Our five goals are:

1. Incorporate planning, implementation of plans and proactive mitigation measures, risk management, resource stewardship, environmental considerations, and public education as the key elements of effective national drought policy.
2. Improve collaboration among scientists and managers to enhance the effectiveness of observation networks, monitoring, prediction, information delivery, and applied research and to foster public understanding of and preparedness for drought.
3. Develop and incorporate comprehensive insurance and financial strategies into drought preparedness plans.
4. Maintain a safety net of emergency relief that emphasizes sound stewardship of natural resources and self-help.
5. Coordinate drought programs and response effectively, efficiently, and in a customer-oriented manner.

Commitment is required to achieve the goals of national drought policy. That commitment must include resolve by the federal government to provide dependable, long-term funding of the required work and the personnel to carry out the work. Allocation of the funds needed to fulfill such a commitment should be based on consideration of the costs and benefits associated with drought impact-reduction measures.

FROM RELIEF TO READINESS

For years, farmers and ranchers, tribes, public land managers, scientists, economists, small business owners, conservationists and wildlife managers, small and large municipalities, counties, states, regional entities, and the federal government have grappled with the far-reaching consequences of drought. Numerous papers, reports, and books have recorded and analyzed the impacts of drought. They have pointed out over and over again that drought planning and proactive mitigation programs may well reduce the need for huge federal emergency relief expenditures in drought-stricken regions—usually to assist farmers and ranchers and rebuild local economies. They have also indicated that planning and proactive mitigation may lessen conflicts over competition for water during drought.

Many states and local governments include drought in their comprehensive water management, land-use, and long-term planning strategies. Some have devised separate drought plans. These government entities know best about local resources and local priorities, and they know how to communicate with their constituencies and stimulate people to action. Some farmers, ranchers, and other businesses also incorporate drought concerns into their risk-management assessments. Private entrepreneurs and nonprofit groups with an interest in water management and environmental issues work with governments to carry out drought education projects and water conservation initiatives that rely on the cooperation of the general public. In response to individual challenges over the years, Congress has enacted laws to create federal programs aimed at lessening the impacts of drought, and special congressional appropriations of federal taxpayer dollars underwrite much of the drought relief.

Despite such well-intentioned efforts, from a national perspective this country relies on a patchy approach to reduce the impacts of drought. And despite the major role that the federal government plays in responding to drought events, no single federal agency is in a lead or coordinating position regarding drought. State, local, and tribal governments must deal individually and separately with each federal agency involved in drought assistance. Crisis management—rather than planning and proactive mitigation measures—often characterizes the federal response to drought emergencies.

Droughts can last for years. This is one reason why it is difficult to determine if a loss in, say, landscape investments is because of drought or because of declining disposable income from an economic downturn. But even the most conservative estimates of the impacts of drought are large. The Commission found several studies of the federal government's response to the major post-World War II droughts. We updated those findings of federal drought expenditures to 1998 dollars and include them here. "Government Response to Drought in the United States: Lessons from the Mid-1970's" (June 1984), a report funded by the National Science Foundation, indicated the federal government spent $3.3 billion responding to the 1953-1956 drought. That study and "Managing Resource Scarcity" by the Western Governors' Policy Office also indicated that federal drought response cost at least $6.5 billion during the 1976-1977 drought and about $6 billion during the 1988- 1989 drought. The last figure does not include crop insurance payments. Thus, extraordinary federal expenses for drought alone over the 1952-1988 period averaged at least half a billion dollars per year.

Clearly there were other costs. "Drought and Natural Resources Management in the United States: Impacts and Implications of the 1987-

1989 Drought" (Riebsame, Changnon, and Karl) documented a reduction in crop production of nearly $20 billion and an increase in food prices of more than $12 billion because of the 1988 drought. The report also noted that low flows on the Mississippi in 1988 caused barge shipping prices to double and triple, leading to an estimated $1 billion in increased transportation costs. At the Commission's Austin hearing, Texas Agriculture Commissioner Susan Combs stated that the 1996 and 1998 droughts in her state caused a loss of $4 billion in direct income, with the total impact to the state's economy close to $11 billion.

Drought near Bracketville, Texas, in 1980 ravaged the landscape, almost drying up this livestock watering pond.

OPPORTUNITY FOR ACTION

In the National Drought Policy Act of 1998, Congress presented this country with a significant opportunity. The law recognized the need to prepare for and lessen the severe impacts of drought on the American people and the environment. It created the National Drought Policy Commission to advise Congress on formulation of national drought policy based on preparedness, mitigation, and risk management rather than on crisis management, which is the corner-stone of current federal responses to drought. The Act also directed the Commission to present a strategy that shifts from *ad hoc* federal action toward a "systematic process similar to those for other natural disasters" and to integrate federal programs with "ongoing state, local, and tribal programs."

The National Drought Policy Act assigned eight tasks to the Commission, listed on the next page. The remainder of the report describes the consequences of drought, discusses drought definitions, and presents our findings of needs related to droughts, followed by conclusions of unmet needs and lack of coordination, and recommendations for action.

> *The law that created the National Drought Policy Commission called for national drought policy based on preparedness rather than on crisis management, which is the cornerstone of current federal responses to drought.*

CHARGE TO THE NATIONAL DROUGHT POLICY COMMISSION

- Determine, in consultation with the National Drought Mitigation Center in Lincoln, Nebraska, and other appropriate entities, what needs exist on the federal, state, local, and tribal levels to prepare for and respond to drought emergencies.
- Review all existing federal laws and programs relating to drought.
- Review pertinent state, local, and tribal laws and programs relating to drought.
- Determine what differences exist between the needs of those affected by drought and Charge to the National Drought Policy Commission federal laws and programs designed to mitigate the impacts of and respond to drought.
- Collaborate with the Western Drought Coordination Council and other appropriate entities to consider regional drought initiatives and the application of such initiatives at the national level.
- Recommend how federal drought laws and programs can be better integrated with ongoing state, local, and tribal programs into a comprehensive national policy to mitigate the impacts of and respond to drought emergencies without diminishing the right of states to control water through state law and considering the need to protect the environment.
- Recommend how to improve public awareness of the need for drought mitigation and develop a coordinated approach to drought mitigation

and response by governmental and nongovernmental entities, including academic, private, and nonprofit interests.

- Recommend whether all federal drought preparation and response programs should be consolidated under one existing federal agency and, if so, identify such agency.

CONSEQUENCES OF DROUGHT

Drought is perhaps the most obstinate and pernicious of the dramatic events that Nature conjures up. It can last longer and extend across larger areas than hurricanes, tornadoes, floods, and earthquakes. At its most severe, drought creates vast, windblown dust bowls—eroding the landscape, damaging terrestrial and aquatic wildlife habitat, contributing to widespread wildfire, causing hundreds of millions of dollars in losses, and dashing hopes and dreams.

Drought may be the last straw in driving farm and ranch families off their land and livestock producers out of business. It brings hardship to water-dependent enterprises such as commercial fishing, marinas, river outfitters and guides, landscapers, golf courses, and water theme parks. In many small communities, downturns in farming, ranching, and recreation have a rippling effect, causing loss of income for seed and implement retailers, recreation equipment suppliers, and Main Street businesses—from grocery stores to clothing outlets, entertainment operations, restaurants, and banks. This in turn creates revenue shortfalls for local governments.

Drought can have devastating impacts on the lives of migrant agricultural workers and people employed in seasonal, recreation-dependent jobs. Drought can lead to tough decisions regarding allocation of water and result in stringent water-use limitations. Drought can also cause problems in ensuring safe drinking water as well as adequate water supplies for municipal, county, and rural fire-fighting efforts and for the dilution of wastewater effluent.

In large managed river basins and water systems such as the Columbia, Missouri, the state and federal California reservoir systems, the Colorado River, the Apalachicola-Chattahoochee-Flint, and others, drought creates or exacerbates conflicts about who should get water. The most common conflicts pit older, established uses such as agriculture and navigation against newer uses such as recreation and water for growing municipal populations, and water for direct human use against water for ecosystems.

DEFINING DROUGHT

The definition of what drought is and what drought is not has profound implications for the environment and all segments of society, yet it may be different for each. Many attempts have been made to develop a comprehensive and meaningful definition. A generic definition provides a starting point: "Drought is a persistent and abnormal moisture deficiency having adverse impacts on vegetation, animals, or people."

The public perceives "drought" as a serious departure from normal water conditions, a departure that requires a public response to reduce negative impacts. For that reason, public declarations of drought are often triggered by specific and well-defined conditions, such as a specific reservoir elevation on a specific date. In some cases, there are well-defined exit points that trigger a resumption of normal activity. These "drought triggers" become the practical definition of drought for a particular region and for specific issues. Defining these triggers is an inseparable part of planning for and responding to droughts. Once these triggers are defined, a region is much better able to estimate the costs, expected frequency, and risks of drought response.

The Commission has found that in reality, drought is defined differently in different situations. For example, two months without rainfall during the growing season may result in serious drought conditions for farmers and homeowners in the eastern half of the country. The same dry period may be normal for those in the West, where water users may be more concerned with reservoir levels, which in turn are dependent on winter snow pack levels.

In addition, the definition of what is drought has different functions depending on the goals to be achieved. For the purposes of planning and proactive mitigation, communities, business owners, and individuals need fact-based information that helps define strategies to lessen the potential impacts of drought. The declaration that "this is drought" triggers certain actions such as restrictions on the availability of water to users and activation of government response programs.

National drought policy must therefore define drought so that it meets the needs of diverse water users and for diverse functions. It must be flexible enough to include a variety of drought situations. It must also be specific enough to distinguish between those situations that are true drought emergencies and those that are normal cyclical conditions.

> *National drought policy must be flexible enough to include a variety of drought situations. It must also be specific enough to distinguish between those situations that are true drought emergencies and those that are normal cyclical conditions.*

Because of the extremely diverse climates, topographies, watersheds, water sources, and water uses within this country, we find it impractical to define specific drought thresholds that could act as triggers for drought actions for various parts of the country. However, we recognize that a suite of objective triggers similar to those used by the Australian Drought Policy Review Task Force has the advantage of taking much of the politics out of drought-response decisions. As in Australia, these should be both supply-type triggers, reflecting moisture deficiencies caused by acts of nature (lack of rain, excessive temperatures), as well as demand-type triggers reflecting drought impacts.

Examples of current supply-type triggers used in general to define drought or trigger actions related to potential drought include: precipitation less than 60% of normal for the season or present water year (used by the National Weather Service's Western Region); precipitation less than 85% of normal over the past six months (used by the National Weather Service's Eastern Region); the Palmer Drought Index -2.0 or less; and consolidated drought indices at the 20th percentile or less (used by the Drought Monitor). For federal action, more rigid triggers such as 5th percentile drought might be appropriate, reflecting truly unusual circumstances.

Examples of demand (impact) based triggers include water supply less than 60% of normal (used by the National Weather Service's Western Region) and various crop loss thresholds used by the U.S. Department of Agriculture.

"Stored Water" and "Natural Water" Droughts

We note that the United States experiences two types of drought. "Stored water" droughts occur when large stores of water in man-made reservoirs, natural lakes, and groundwater aquifers are depleted by very long, unusually low periods of precipitation. "Natural water" droughts happen quickly and fairly frequently after just a few weeks or months of below-normal rainfall.

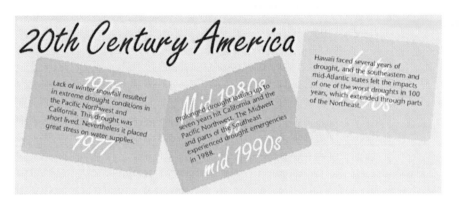

20th Century America

1976 Lack of winter snowfall resulted in extreme drought conditions in the Pacific Northwest and California. This drought was short lived. Nevertheless it placed great stress on water supplies. 1977

Mid 1980s Prolonged drought lasting up to seven years hit California and the Pacific Northwest. The Midwest and parts of the Southeast experienced drought emergencies in 1988. mid 1990s

Hawaii faced several years of drought, and the southeastern and mid-Atlantic states felt the impacts of one of the worst droughts in 100 years, which extended through parts of the Northeast.

Those who share stored water are rarely affected by less than normal precipitation because the systems are designed to provide water during those times. But the very success of such systems creates a new kind of vulnerability to drought that was revealed in the Northeast during drought in the 1960s, the 1976-1977 and 1987-1992 droughts in California, droughts around the country in the late 1980s, and the mid-Atlantic, southeastern, and northeastern drought in 1999. Specific issues vary, but the pattern is common.

- People without enough stored water build reservoirs or tap into surface or groundwater storage.
- Reliable water helps support greater populations and more diverse uses of water. Hydro-power dams create popular fishing and boating lakes and valuable lake view property. Reservoir operating policies are supposed to assure minimum flows for fish and wastewater dilution when there would otherwise not be enough water in the stream. Cities and farmers increase their withdrawals as they prosper and grow.
- An unusually long dry period forces reservoir operators to draw down these man-made lakes to support withdrawals for cities and farms, produce hydropower, and keep enough water in navigation channels

for barges to float. But homes and businesses around the lake now have views of mud flats. Boat ramps no longer reach the water. Lake fisheries suffer when releases are made for riverine species.

- No one can tell when it will rain enough to reverse this trend, so water deliveries have to be reduced, but to whom first and by how much?
- There may be a conflict between fairness and good economic policy in making water allocations. The newest water uses may generate more income and tax revenue than the oldest established uses. Such conflicts are normally resolved on a case-by-case basis.

Public testimony at the Commission's hearing in Los Angeles and comments from the Army Corps of Engineers pointed out that stored water system managers develop drought contingency plans that call for the staged curtailment of the least important uses of water (such as lawn watering) during droughts. Communities may elect to accept these drought-related reductions rather than add reservoir capacity to meet growing needs.

Stored water managers consider the risks associated with the probability of system failure, the uncertain effectiveness of drought curtailment measures, uncertainty in estimates of drought severity and duration, and the tolerance of utility customers for water use curtailments. These concepts are not routinely applied to manage drought impacts on agriculture, but they could be. As Guy Martin of the Western Urban Water Coalition advised the Commission, "Overall, we believe there is a missed opportunity to link the resources of the urban water sector with the agricultural sector. While the end water use may be different, the techniques necessary to plan for, conduct, assess, monitor and implement conservation techniques to alleviate drought impacts cover all sectors."

Natural water droughts mostly affect people such as farmers and ranchers, forest and woodlot owners and managers, customers of many water systems, and the owners of water-dependent businesses who rely on direct precipitation or unregulated stream flows. These people are usually the first to feel the effects of drought.

Farmers who do not have irrigation systems, for example, take a risk when they plant crops, assuming that there will be enough rain throughout the growing season to produce a successful harvest. For the most part, the risk is based on how often there has been enough rain in the past. Long-term predictions of precipitation are still too unreliable to reduce that risk significantly.

> *The definition of what drought is and what drought is not has profound implications for the environment and all segments of society, yet it may be different for each. Many attempts have been made to develop a comprehensive and meaningful definition. A generic definition provides a starting point: "Drought is a persistent and abnormal moisture deficiency having adverse impacts on vegetation, animals, or people."*

At our hearings across the country, we were told of several gaps among existing programs and the needs of farmers and ranchers who do not rely on irrigation:

- Farmers and ranchers may lack information about local climate and drought conditions and predictions. Many also lack basic soil information; a soil survey remains to be completed for approximately 10% of the country. These deficiencies can limit a farmer's or rancher's ability to make timely decisions on the types of crops to plant or whether to reduce stocking rates on the range.
- Many farmers and ranchers do not have access to available information and other resources to develop and implement a water conservation/drought plan. Less than 10% of farmers and ranchers are receiving technical assistance to help them develop and implement such plans, and an even smaller number are receiving cost-share assistance for these plans.
- Federal crop insurance covers only the "primary" crops grown and does not extend to other crops or to livestock. We learned that during drought the price of transporting feed after stored supplies are used up is prohibitive in many cases, as is the price of transporting water to livestock where ponds have gone dry.

We heard too that when drought affects the incomes of farmers and ranchers and the owners of water-dependent businesses, it also affects the incomes of nearby local businesses. Such economic impacts may extend further to nearby cities.

FINDINGS

Our assessments of federal, regional, tribal, state, and local drought-related programs indicate that there is broad-based understanding of the value and benefits of drought preparedness. The assessments also revealed that, overall, federal drought assistance to states, local governments, tribes, and individuals is primarily relief oriented. Few federal programs are designed to provide drought preparedness assistance. Furthermore, public testimony strongly indicated varying degrees of satisfaction with the federal programs.

Our deliberations have convinced us that this country can and must do better to prepare for drought in the future. At our public hearings, more than one hundred people testified on behalf of urban and rural water associations, tribes, federal agencies, state and county governments, municipalities, livestock production and farmer associations, and conservation groups. With respect to U.S. Department of Agriculture programs, we heard similar criticisms from farmers, ranchers, and tribal representatives in Austin and El Paso, Texas, Atlanta, Georgia, Washington, D.C., and Billings, Montana. These people expressed concern that the application process for agricultural drought assistance programs is too cumbersome, that it takes too long to make decisions, and that placing federal decision-making outside the local level often results in disconnection among the applicants and the programs. Livestock producers consistently pointed out that their operations are excluded from agricultural assistance programs. Representatives from state, county, and local agricultural agencies noted communication and coordination challenges within the Department of Agriculture. On balance, we also heard about successful programs in the Department of Agriculture, the Bureau of Reclamation, and other federal agencies.

This testimony, combined with written comments submitted independently, helped identify gaps among federal, state, local, regional, and tribal programs and the people those programs are designed to serve. We also reviewed information and analyses prepared by the five Working Groups—agriculture; environment; municipal and industrial water; local government, community, and business; and monitoring and prediction—that we established to assist us in assessing state, regional, local, tribal, and federal drought programs and related laws. Nonfederal and federal experts in various aspects of drought, including staff of the National Drought Mitigation Center, formed the Working Groups. The Interagency Contacts Group coordinated the Working Groups and worked with the Commission's staff to prepare this chapter. This work also identified gaps in service delivery.

The discussion below summarizes our findings. We emphasize that current programs may cover gaps in service delivery partially in some cases and more fully in some locations than in others. Yet in many critical areas of drought preparedness, we heard that current federal programs do not provide any measurable assistance. Collectively, the gaps are significant and merit attention and remedies.

> *The Commission met in Los Angeles, California, Scottsdale, Arizona, and Washington, D.C., and several times through teleconference technology. Public hearings were held in Los Angeles, California, El Paso and Austin Texas, Atlanta, Georgia, Billings, Montana, and Washington, D.C. All meetings of the Commission and all public hearings were announced in advance, according to federal procedures, and were open to the public.*

Drought Programs

States

We learned that as of June 1999, 30 states had drought plans, with most of those oriented to relief rather than preparedness. Two states had delegated drought planning to local authorities, and three states were developing drought plans. In general, the states with larger numbers of people and resources at risk of drought tend to have more detailed state programs.

Five states reported that they have some drought funding mechanisms not tied to a federal administrative or presidential declaration of drought emergency. For example, Texas has a Community Development Program Disaster Relief Fund that can provide up to $350,000 in grant money for small communities (less than 50,000 residents) to support their permanent water supply infrastructure.

Our assessments pointed out that in most states, drought responsibilities are normally located in the agencies that house the functions of agriculture, natural resources, water management, environment, or emergency management. Fewer than five states reported that they have independent, designated drought coordinators, while more than 20 have drought task forces. Wisconsin, for example, lacks a specific drought plan but does use an ad hoc drought task force. In Maine, representatives from the U.S. Geological Survey and the University of Maine Water Research Program issued a report in January 2000 that recommended the Maine Drought Task Force develop a master plan or vision. New Mexico has completed a drought plan in conjunction with the Bureau of Reclamation, which provided assistance in developing the plan. Arizona and Hawaii are currently involved in a similar process with the Bureau.

California has a well-developed process for general water management planning through the Central Valley Improvement Act and the state's Urban Water Management Planning Act. These acts create a key link for water shortage planning and coordination. The urban water legislation, for example, requires water purveyors serving more than 3,000 acre-feet annually or more than 3,000 connections to prepare plans to demonstrate how they would respond to cut-backs of up to 50% in their supplies in the event of drought or natural disasters. The plans must be updated every five years and are submitted to the California Department of Water Resources.

Utah is one example of a state that approaches drought from several angles. The state recently completed a state drought plan that also included several counties and was funded by the Bureau of Reclamation. In comments submitted to the Commission, state officials noted that state law related to flood control and drought emergencies grants Utah counties the authority to levy taxes and generate funds to aid in programs to increase precipitation. Utah's Department of Agriculture and Food has a low-interest loan program available to assist drought-stricken farmers and ranchers. The loans help fund measures such as installation of pipelines, tanks, and troughs; construction and deepening of wells; development of springs or seeps; construction of tail water recovery pits for irrigation systems; and correction of conservation problems on farmland caused by severe drought. Utah Department of Agriculture and Food officials suggested that federal assistance should be available to transport resources from areas not experiencing drought to areas that are in a drought.

In written comments and through testimony during the Commission's public hearings, state officials often noted that federal assistance could go far to help localities and states prepare for drought, including assistance for planning and proactive mitigation measures. In their comments to the Commission, the governors of Iowa and Missouri stated that "coordination among the various existing federal programs is necessary, as is coordination between federal agencies and the states." The two governors emphasized that such coordination is preferable to "new federal programs with regulatory authority over the states."

Regional Entities

There are several regional entities that either focus on drought or include drought as a major component of their work. The Western Drought Coordination Council, for example, presented the Commission with a set of potential actions that focus on drought planning, impact-reduction measures, and effective response. And the Tarrant Regional Water District (Texas) incorporates simulated drought exercises as a training tool in its drought planning.

The Commission received a number of comments that encouraged regional drought planning or incorporation of drought concerns into comprehensive regional water management plans. The comments echoed earlier recommendations of the 1990 National Science Foundation's Drought Water Management Workshop. Participants at the workshop concluded, "The real need is to institutionalize drought management into improved overall water management systems." They stated that attempts to understand and address drought problems will be unsuccessful unless the larger context of which they are an inseparable part is also understood and addressed. The Army Corps of Engineers drew a similar conclusion in the first year (1989) of the National Drought Study.

> In 1999, Kentucky experienced the driest July-September period in 105 years of record. Yet none of the water systems in the state required outside emergency assistance. Officials credit Kentucky's drought management planning program, adopted in 1993—a program that paid off through pre-drought water conservation measures and better preparedness for citizens and communities. The state provided financial and technical assistance as well as detailed guidelines to assist communities in developing management plans. Those plans called at a minimum for water systems to project future water demand; evaluate the adequacy of water supplies and infrastructure; and, where gaps existed among current capabilities and future needs, determine the best means and the associated costs to meet those needs.

The regional approach has been undertaken in the past and survives today. On June 14, 1965, during the height of the 1960s drought in the Northeast, New York City stopped releases from its Delaware River reservoirs to maintain its withdrawal rate. With less fresh water flowing past Philadelphia, there was a risk that salt water would be drawn into Philadelphia's water supply system. In August, President Lyndon Johnson convened a special meeting of governors and mayors from the Delaware Basin that led to emergency measures for managing the Delaware. The President then asked Congress for funds to start the North Atlantic Regional Study, a framework on which subsequent basin and project justification studies in the North Atlantic region would be based.

The six-county, multi-municipal Metropolitan Water District of Southern California incorporates drought planning and preparedness in its comprehensive Integrated Resources Plan and Water Surplus and Demand Management Plan. Testimony at our hearing in Los Angeles noted that the District emphasizes citizen and customer participation in water conservation as well as long-term water supply and resource management programs for a region receiving 10 to 15 inches of rainfall in an average year.

Metropolitan's plans ensure reliable water supplies for more than 16 million people (municipal, industrial, commercial, and agricultural uses) despite weather, regulatory, or disaster-based drought pressures. The southern California region has spent $8 billion for water conservation, recycling, and storage projects since 1982, and those investments appear to be paying off. The region is using less water today than in 1975, even though the population increased by 5 million people from 1975 to 1999.

The Denver, Colorado area boasts a similar success. The Denver Water Authority told us that their year-round water conservation program "has reduced water demand over the last 20 years. Even though the population of our service area has increased from 840,000 in 1980 to 970,000 in 1998, the total water we deliver has stayed relatively flat at around 77 billion gallons per year. We attribute much of this to our water conservation efforts."

A month before the August meeting, the President had signed the Water Resources Planning Act, which established the Water Resources Council. The Act and the North Atlantic Regional Study were the predecessors of the current federal rules for water resources planning that emphasize a basin perspective, multi-objective assessments, public involvement, and risk assessment. Several federal/state river basin organizations were formed under Title II of the Water Resources Planning Act, but supporting federal funds were terminated in 1981. The organizations that survive take a variety of forms designed by their member states to address specific issues, often including drought. Their diversity is demonstrated in the following sample from the northeastern quadrant of the country.

- The Delaware River Basin Commission, created in 1961, is active in drought management. The Commission informed us they have coordinated efforts to negotiate drought mitigation programs throughout the Delaware River Basin. Such initiatives help cities and states in the basin prepare for, not simply respond to, drought. The programs have been responsible for preserving billions of gallons of reservoir storage while maintaining streamflows during drought periods.

- The Susquehanna River Basin Commission, created in 1970, was built on a statute similar to that of the Delaware River Basin Commission and is likewise engaged in drought management. The Commission presents the opportunity for major water users and other interested parties to assess the effectiveness of drought management measures, list the lessons learned in managing drought, and compile and distribute the findings to key decision makers. The Commission told us that they recently developed a plan to coordinate drought management activities among the signatory agencies in the river basin. The next stage of the plan will develop strategies to mitigate environmental impacts resulting from drought. Those strategies incorporate what the Commission described as detailed instream flow needs assessments that are cutting-edge technologies in environmental drought management.

- Congress ratified an interstate compact for the Potomac River, but the member states did not sign it. They rely instead on the Interstate Compact on the Potomac River formed under the older (1940) Potomac Valley Compact. This organization helped broker a water supply agreement among Maryland, Virginia, and the District of Columbia that relies on joint operation and annual drought exercises to assure dependable water supply. It has demonstrated that coordination and management of water resources on a regional multi-jurisdictional basis during drought periods can allow a major metropolitan area to sustain itself. This group emphasized that its coordination efforts involve "the development and maintenance of a drought preparedness plan and the annual exercise of that plan." The exercise is undertaken "to refine [the plan's] relevance and bring newly hired and replacement personnel from the several jurisdictions and water suppliers up to date on this critical issue of regional water resources management."

- The Ohio River Basin Commission, established in 1971, is an informal structure that serves as a forum to discuss, study, develop, and coordinate regional policies and positions on common interstate water issues. Member states include Illinois, Indiana, Kentucky, Maryland, North Carolina, Ohio, Pennsylvania, Virginia, and West

Virginia. The Commission should not be confused with the Ohio River Valley Sanitation Commission, which was formed in 1948 under an inter-state compact to manage water quality.

Localities

A sample survey of county officials conducted by the National Association of Counties (NACO) in 1999 indicated that county governments primarily rely on federal programs for drought assistance. More than seventy-five percent of the 177 respondents indicated that they use federal programs to respond during drought emergencies. This represents a small sample of the 3,066 counties across the country. However, it is a starting place to understand local government needs.

Twenty percent of the 177 respondents have county or city drought assistance programs or regulations that include drought emergency response as well as water conservation plans incorporating drought contingency procedures. Most counties have emergency procedures for disasters, including drought, and communication channels to get information to their populations.

County officials must try to manage fragmented federal assistance programs to help their constituents. Links may exist between the U.S. Department of Agriculture and farmers through Cooperative Extension offices, the Department's Service Centers, and Resource Conservation and Development Councils. But coordination and communication may not be efficient, or extend beyond traditional agricultural users, especially during a drought emergency. The Commission heard considerable testimony from county and other local officials that these linkages are often laden with bureaucracy, delays, and program guidelines that do not reflect environmental, resource, temperature, and climate variability across the country. In Billings, Montana, for example, the important drought-related factor of wind is not included in the Department of Agriculture's assessment process. In addition, many people testified to the significant lack of weather and streamflow gages and data in general that are needed to substantiate, review, and make decisions about their applications for agricultural assistance.

Counties, towns, and rural areas are facing suburban growth and development. To provide public health, safety, and welfare services, counties with increasing populations must be able to plan for future needs. A local government's ability to plan for drought is dramatically improved if technical data, tools, and resources are available.

Local governments must also inform and educate their constituents of the need for drought planning, especially when an emergency is not imminent.

Many local governments have public information programs on water resources that could be supplemented with information about drought.

Communities can plan to minimize impacts when a drought reduces water supplies. With the exception of the city of Santa Barbara and surrounding communities in California during the 1987-1992 drought, droughts have not created a potable water emergency in large cities since the 1960s. This is in part because of the amount of planning large cities do. But emergency conditions—not enough water for minimal household uses—may still arise in small communities when droughts are longer or more severe than anticipated or when other factors unexpectedly interrupt or pollute water supplies.

Examples of Localities with Drought-related Programs:

Thirty-five percent of the 177 counties that responded to the National Association of Counties' 1999 sample survey were from Georgia. Others included:

Graham County, Arizona	Becker County, Minnesota	Williamson County, Texas
Navajo County, Arizona	Yellowstone County, Montana	Gloucester County, Virginia
Yuba County, California	Benson County, North Dakota	Marion County, West Virginia
Bannock County, Idaho	Muskingum County, Ohio	Dane County, Wisconsin
Lake County, Indiana	Lancaster County, Pennsylvania	

We also heard about many drought preparedness measures developed by municipalities, including those in New York City, Scottsdale, Arizona, and Denver, Colorado. More than 400 local agencies in California engage in drought preparedness efforts, including agencies in the cities of Los Angeles, San Francisco, and San Diego.

At the Commission's hearing in Atlanta, Georgia, County Commissioner George Bird of Candler County, Georgia, described the Georgia Water Management Campaign. The Campaign's mission is to enhance the abilities of local governments to manage and protect water resources by translating water management policies into local government decision-making capabilities, guidance, and technical assistance. To achieve this mission, the Campaign developed outreach tools such as public

---

service announcements, videos, and case studies and convened summits on water issues for local officials. The Campaign's 21 members of the Local Government Advisory Board serve as ambassadors and provide overall guidance. The Campaign was created through a partnership among the Georgia Environmental Protection Division, Georgia Environmental Facilities Authority, and the Association of County Commissioners of Georgia. As Commissioner Bird said, "Water issues are a developing priority for local governments. Education and public input are key to local decision making."

Some cities use data from the U.S. Geological Survey and the National Oceanic and Atmospheric Administration in developing and implementing their plans. And federal water agencies can sell space in existing federal reservoirs for urban water supplies. In cities near such reservoirs, this may be the least expensive way to get more water. Small communities and the millions of "self-supplied" Americans, who rely on their own wells, are likely to have problems during prolonged drought. Small water systems tend to be vulnerable because they have only one source of water. Such systems may also face high per-customer costs to meet the latest federal safe drinking water standards. These factors have encouraged the takeover of small systems by large systems where it is economically feasible. But areas with very low population density remain at risk. Some small communities may be able to modify existing watershed structures, initially designed only for flood control, to provide storage for municipal and industrial water.

Tribes

On tribal lands, dominant uses of water include agriculture, recreation, municipal and industrial, and social, cultural, and religious purposes. Tribes also support water use for fish and wildlife and other environmental goals.

There are approximately 560 federally recognized tribes within the United States—306 in the conterminous 48 states, with 289 of those west of the Mississippi River where 95 percent of all tribal trust land is located. The Department of the Interior notes that tribal lands, including official reservations, currently cover about 55 million acres, or roughly three percent of the country except for Alaska and Hawaii. The largest area is the Navajo Nation, while some federally recognized tribes have no land. The states with the highest tribal populations are Oklahoma, California, Arizona, New Mexico, and Alaska.

The Commission was informed of various proactive drought mitigation activities developed at the local level, often in partnership with state and federal agencies through technical and financial incentive programs. In Los Angeles, "Second Nature: Adapting LA's Landscape for Sustainable Living" is a program run by the nonprofit TreePeople organization. The program involves young people in urban landscape retrofits such as planting trees and citizens and businesses in capturing storm water and adjusting runoff patterns for residences and commercial buildings. In these and other ways, TreePeople reinforces the principle that locally developed solutions can be effective.

By any measure, the scope of tribal drought issues in the West is immense. Tribes have experienced the vagaries of climate on this continent for many thousands of years, and more recent times have proved to be no exception. Flexibility was the key to adaptation and relative self-sufficiency in earlier times. When the ability to cope in one place was exceeded, tribes moved, later returning when climate permitted. Since the loss of many of their ancestral lands, however, such flexibility is no longer possible for the tribes.

Some tribes are turning to planning as a viable means of lessening the impacts of drought on tribal lands and populations. But others expressed their concerns that criteria for national drought policy might compromise their cultural or religious beliefs, and they specifically asked that this not occur. Some tribes were also reluctant to disclose water-related information because of ongoing negotiations over water rights. They asked that any national drought policy be sensitive to these issues and that the Commission uphold the special relationship that tribes have with the federal government.

As a result of our outreach effort, we found that six tribes—the Hopi Tribe, Hualapai Nation, Kaibab-Paiute Tribe, Navajo Nation, San Carlos Apache Tribe, and Zuni Pueblo—are in the process of developing drought contingency plans through cooperative agreements with the Bureau of Reclamation.

Based on these experiences, developing drought plans can cost from $25,000 to $200,000.

But in Billings, Montana, representatives from seven tribes consistently reported frustration in not being able to rely on the procedures and processes associated with the "Government-to-Government" Executive Order signed by President Clinton. They described the bureaucratic quagmire associated with the Bureau of Indian Affairs. Most tribal witnesses also explained that eligibility criteria and cost-share rates in many current drought-related programs must be modified to address specific tribal situations. They emphasized that such programs must be adequately funded.

We learned from comments submitted by tribes from Florida to Alaska and from the Intertribal Agriculture Council that many tribal lands lack current soil survey, streamgaging, and range condition information. Such information is critical to basic planning as well as drought planning. Some tribes indicated that they lack access to snow amount, soil moisture, and stream flow information needed in planning and for triggering emergency response efforts. Many tribes noted the need for technical and financial assistance to plan and implement conservation measures such as wells, springs, and ponds for livestock water; cross fences for grazing management; and other practices to enhance wildlife and protect against wildfire. They emphasized that this assistance must be easily and locally accessible to tribal members.

Federal Government

We found that 88 drought-related federal programs were funded within the past ten years. We classed those programs into four broad program categories: (1) preparedness, including planning and mitigation; (2) information, including monitoring/ prediction and research; (3) insurance; and (4) emergency response. Seven of these programs provide assistance for drought planning, 42 for drought mitigation, 22 for drought-related monitoring/prediction and research, and 47 for response. These numbers total more than 88 because some programs cover more than one facet of drought. For example, some of the mitigation programs also contain drought planning and response elements.

Planning

Many people who commented during all of our hearings recognized the importance of comprehensive long-term strategies that incorporate drought planning and plan implementation. We also heard often that drought should be a consideration in comprehensive water management planning. In addition, Jennifer Salisbury, the Cabinet Secretary of the New Mexico Energy, Minerals, & Natural Resources Department, urged us to consider forest resource stewardship programs as drought preparedness and mitigation programs.

> *Many people who commented during our proceedings recognized the importance of comprehensive long-term strategies that incorporate drought planning and plan implementation.*

The three federal entities with the greatest federal responsibilities when drought occurs are the U.S. Department of Agriculture, the Bureau of Reclamation, and the U.S. Army Corps of Engineers. Title II of Public Law 102-250 (The Reclamation States Emergency Drought Relief Act of 1991) authorized the Bureau of Reclamation to prepare or participate in the preparation of cooperative drought contingency plans for the prevention or mitigation of adverse effects of drought conditions in consultation with other appropriate federal and state officials (of all 50 states and U.S. territories); tribes; and public, private, and local entities. Until very recently, these efforts were funded from emergency or supplemental funds. In its Fiscal Year 2000 budget, the Bureau of Reclamation requested $500,000 for the program. Congress appropriated $3,000,000, but restricted use of those funds primarily to the leasing of water. The Bureau also requested $500,000 in its 2001 budget.

Public Law 92-251 allows the U.S. Army Corps of Engineers to develop water resource plans for states, tribes, and territories. The plans can cover any aspect of water and water-related land issues, including drought preparedness if that is what a state or tribe wants. Funding is limited to $500,000 annually for each state or tribe. Individual studies (there may be more than one per state or tribe per year) generally cost $25,000 to $75,000, an amount that is split 50-50 between the state or tribe and the Corps. The priorities of the nonfederal sponsor determine which aspect of water management will be studied. Topics of studies conducted in recent years include water supply and demand, water quality, environmental conservation/restoration, wetlands evaluation, dam safety/failure, flood damage, flood plain management, coastal zone management/protection, and harbors/ports. This Corps program funded the preparatory work that preceded the virtual drought exercise in Tarrant County, Texas (see above, "Regional Entities").

The 1935 Soil Conservation Act authorized the U.S. Department of Agriculture to provide assistance for individual farmers and ranchers to develop and implement conservation plans. This legislation responded to the persistent drought of the 1930s and the resulting "Dust Bowl" caused by severe wind erosion. For 65 years, hundreds of thousands of farmers and ranchers have received technical and financial assistance to address critical resource needs. Under this voluntary program, assistance is provided at the request of the farmer and normally for specific needs such as erosion, water quality, or irrigation problems that the farmer identifies.

Limited authorities and funds as well as lack of coordination among and within federal agencies hinder these planning efforts. For the Bureau of

Reclamation's Drought Program, requests for planning assistance far outweigh available funds, and the program provides technical assistance only, not direct grants. The Corps of Engineers water resource planning program is not specifically targeted to drought needs, and drought is not receiving much attention in these efforts. Witnesses told us that there is too much program bureaucracy within the Department of Agriculture. Tribal representatives expressed appreciation for the Department's current effort to place offices on tribal lands, but stated they are far behind their non-tribal counterparts.

We heard, too, that developing a drought plan or incorporating drought concerns into a more comprehensive water management plan is of little value unless the plan is implemented. Successful implementation of community drought plans requires practice, particularly when the people who are responsible for responding to drought may not be the same from drought to drought. Enough time passes between droughts that the issues change, water use changes, and professional staff members retire or move to new jobs. Many of the entities involved in drought response during the late 1990s, for example, were also involved in drought response during the late 1980s, but very few of the same people were still participating. As the Army Corps of Engineers, the Denver Water Authority, and the Interstate Compact on the Potomac River told us, communities need to prepare plans for drought and then exercise them, like fire drills, to keep the plan up to date and train new staff.

Several of these points were reinforced at the Commission's hearing in Atlanta, Georgia, by Dr. Anne Steinemann, an assistant professor at the Georgia Institute of Technology Graduate City Planning Program. From her study of more than 100 drought plans in the Southeast, she concluded in part that "even the most technically sophisticated and detailed plans with a lot of data may be ineffective if water officials and stakeholders can't or won't implement these measures...." Dr. Steinemann also told the Commission that drought planning often suffers from lack of "agency staff experienced and expert in drought" and that "drought plans can't be developed without consulting the people who have institutional experience in managing drought."

NATIONAL DROUGHT MITIGATION CENTER

The National Drought Mitigation Center, established in 1995 at the University of Nebraska–Lincoln, helps people and institutions develop and implement measures to reduce society's vulnerability to drought. The Center's director, Dr. Don Wilhite, has estimated that on average 12% of the country is in severe drought each year. The Center emphasizes prevention and risk management rather than crisis management. This approach promotes self-reliance to achieve greater resilience to drought. The Center maintains a continually growing archive of drought-monitoring and planning information on its web site (http://enso.unl.edu/ndmc). That web site also contains products that have been developed with various federal and nonfederal partners and provides links to other drought-related materials. Center staff have developed several drought workshops, both in the United States and internationally, in partnership with the Bureau of Reclamation and other co-sponsors. Federal and nonfederal drought professionals serve as workshop leaders.

We heard from people at our public hearings and in written comments that the Center has been helpful in providing assistance with drought planning, devising proactive mitigation measures, and forming links with other drought professionals. The activities of the Center are funded by an annual grant from the U.S. Department of Agriculture's Cooperative State Research, Education, and Extension Service as well as with supplemental funding through cooperative agreements with other federal entities or through consulting agreements with nonfederal entities.

Mitigation

Mitigation is often associated with actions taken after the fact to remedy damage caused by human or natural disturbances. In the context of this chapter, we use the term "mitigation" to describe actions taken prior to and during drought events to reduce potential impacts and thus reduce the costs of responding to drought. As such, mitigation is an essential, proactive element of drought preparedness.

Proactive drought mitigation comprises a broad range of measures—from the installation of livestock watering ponds on ranches and technologies and methods for capturing storm waterin rural and urban settings to state-of-the-art wastewater treatment that allows reuse of water. We learned during our hearings about many mitigation measures aimed at water conservation during our hearings, including testimony about the "drought-proofing" value of installing ultralow flow toilets in residences in southern California. We note that attempts to repeal plumbing fixture standards, which are important to the success of ultra-low flow toilet programs, or other long-term conservation standards in the 1992 Energy Policy Act should be considered in the larger context of the need for drought preparedness.

We observed an example of state-of-the-art technology at the Scottsdale Water Campus in Arizona and heard about other wastewater treatment and reuse programs from witnesses during our Los Angeles hearing. These types of measures may be aimed specifically at reducing the potential impacts of drought. Or, they may be used to expand water supplies for growing populations, in which case the larger population may still need to plan proactive mitigation of drought impacts.

Within federal government programs, we found that water supply and droughts are considered together. As one example, the Bureau of Reclamation's 2001 budget includes significant amounts for water delivery projects that can help reduce the impacts of drought. These include $65.3 million for the Central Valley Project in California, $33.7 million for the Central Arizona Project, $29.7 million for the Mni Wiconi Project in South Dakota, and $21.3 million for the Garrison Diversion Unit in North Dakota. The budget also contains requests of $22 million for water reclamation and reuse and $2.2 million for the Bureau's small projects loan program. In addition, the Bureau's water conservation program and guidance in the Bureau's tiered pricing handbook has helped several localities carry out water conservation measures to reduce their vulnerability to drought, including tiered pricing strategies.

The U.S. Army Corps of Engineers' total civil works budget for Fiscal Year 2000 is $4 billion (plus $332 million from nonfederal and trust fund receipts). The budget includes $137.7 million for general investigations, nearly $1.4 billion for construction, and $1.9 billion for operation and maintenance. The Corps addresses drought as part of the hydrologic spectrum in its design of projects, including environmental restoration projects, and in the operation of its existing projects. But the Corps has no authority or funding specifically for drought mitigation.

A number of programs within the U.S. Department of Agriculture provide assistance for actions that can lead to drought mitigation, although none are specifically funded for this purpose. The 1954 Small Watershed Act, for example, gave the Department authority to help rural communities address natural resource concerns in small watersheds (less than 250,000 acres in size). Eligible purposes include flood control, water-shed management, water conservation, municipal and industrial water supply, recreation, and fish and wildlife protection. Although the program has broad authorities, a high percentage of the funding has gone to assist local communities in installing flood control measures. There is currently a backlog of requests for assistance totaling nearly $1.4 billion. The annual appropriation is approximately $100 million.

In 1964, Congress passed the Resources Conservation and Development Act to assist local units of government in addressing erosion problems, water management problems, and economic development needs. This program provides technical and financial assistance, but available funding has been limited to technical assistance for the approximately 2,500 local Resource Conservation and Development Councils. The annual appropriation of about $36 million provides each Council with a coordinator position and clerical support.

The 1985 Food Security Act directed the Secretary of Agriculture to enroll 45 million acres of highly erodible lands into the Conservation Reserve Program. This amount was reduced in subsequent farm bills to 36.4 million acres as a cost-savings measure. Farmers receive technical and financial assistance as well as an annual rental payment for installing and maintaining this land in permanent vegetative cover.

In 1996, Congress consolidated several of the Agriculture Department's cost-share programs and created the Environmental Quality Incentives Program. The primary purpose of this program is to help farmers address their water quality problems. But it also provides technical and financial assistance for the installation of water conservation measures as well as livestock watering facilities. Cost-share is provided through long-term agreements that address an entire farm's resource needs. At the Commission's hearing in Billings, Montana, however, witnesses said that the procedures related to this program limit their ability to obtain financial assistance to install proactive drought mitigation measures such as cross fencing and livestock watering developments.

We note that we did not develop specific recommendations for coordinating drought mitigation measures among the different levels of government. We believe that regional intergovernmental groups must take responsibility for such coordination if it is to be effective and accepted. We do make recommendations, however, regarding coordination of federal drought mitigation and other drought-related programs to increase their effectiveness in assisting regional, state, local, and tribal drought planning and mitigation efforts.

Monitoring/prediction and Research

About 22 federal programs have some responsibility for drought monitoring/prediction and research. In relation to monitoring and prediction, these include programs that focus on weather patterns, climate, soil conditions, and streamflow measurements. Examples are three networks— the

Department of Agriculture's Soil Climate Analysis Network (SCAN)/Snow Telemetry Network (SNOTEL), the National Oceanic and Atmospheric Administration/National Weather Service's Cooperative Observer Network (COOP), and the U.S. Geological Survey's streamgaging and groundwater monitoring network. The U.S. Army Corps of Engineers both uses and supports non-Corps federal monitoring systems and has developed its own remote data sensing network to manage its reservoirs.

We heard, however, that such programs are not always available in some areas such as on tribal lands and in remote rural areas. A case in point is the U.S. Geological Survey's streamgaging and groundwater monitoring network. This finding echoes a conclusion reached by an external task force recently assigned to review the Survey's Federal-State Cooperative Water Program. The task force's report (1999) stated, "Current funding for the Cooperative Water Program is not adequate to satisfy all of the needs identified for additional streamflow data, regional groundwater information, updated hydrologic needs and technical publications."

Federal monitoring/prediction programs often join with universities, private institutions, and other nonfederal entities to provide information needed for effective drought preparedness and mitigation. For example, federal programs provide the basic data used by private weather services and other enterprises that play a vital role in supporting farmers and others who are vulnerable to drought. The private weather services use the federally supplied data in detailed predictions that can be tailored to individual farmers and can cover varying time periods as needed. Some private services are using remote-sensing technology that can show farmers areas of crop stress, allowing them to make more efficient decisions about applying fertilizers or irrigating. Such programs should help address the needs of farmers who told us that they rely on irrigation systems and need detailed, localized information (soil moisture, temperature, wind, humidity, evapotranspiration rates) for irrigation scheduling.

As the Western Drought Coordination Council stated in its comments to the Commission, basic weather, water, soil moisture, mountain snow amount, and climate observations are the foundation of the monitoring and assessment activity that alerts the nation to impending drought. The current federal interagency effort to indicate likely drought trends two weeks ahead of time on the drought-monitoring map is a start. But we heard that longer-term predictions would improve services, including prediction maps of drought locations in the medium range (ten days or two weeks) and one to two seasons in advance. The Climate Prediction Center of the National Oceanic and

Atmospheric Administration has begun producing Seasonal Drought Outlook maps, which schematically display likely changes in drought over the next two seasons. Proper use of this product, we were told, depends on a careful explanation of its limitations.

Shirley Gammon, Montana State Conservationist for the U.S. Department of Agriculture, at the Commission's hearing in Billings. Ms. Gammon described the Snowpack Telemetry (SNOTEL) network in Montana, which consists of 123 automated sites that measure the amount of snow pack and the moisture content of the snow. The Commission heard that SNOTEL and other systems such as the U.S. Geological Survey's streamgaging network need to be expanded to cover tribal lands and remote rural areas.

We also heard that the wealth of monitoring and prediction information produced by federal programs and in conjunction with nonfederal partners creates a problem for some users. We heard that drought information and data are often complex and, for the most part, are not currently presented in a standardized format. Such data can also be difficult to find and interpret. This is especially true for individuals, small businesses, and some communities and tribes that do not have ongoing relationships with drought management agencies. Many witnesses at our hearings and written comments submitted independently to the Commission indicated a need for an accessible "gateway" (point of contact) where high-quality, standardized, comprehensible current information and historical data are managed.

In relation to research, we found that this country is blessed with a tremendous storehouse of drought-related scientific and technical know-how. Research programs of the National Oceanic and Atmospheric Administration, the Department of Agriculture, the Department of the Interior, the Environmental Protection Agency, numerous universities, and private institutions— as well as work at the National Drought Mitigation Center— form the basis of knowledge needed to monitor drought and address drought impacts. The U.S. Army Corps of Engineers is also involved in drought-related research. During the National Drought Study (1989-1993), for example, the Corps sponsored research and experiments in many aspects of drought.

However, we often heard that the results of research are not always disseminated in a timely fashion or through easily accessible modes, a criticism similar to that we received concerning monitoring and prediction data and products. Research results as well as technology transfers, we were told, are key to effective drought planning, proactive mitigation, emergency response, and drought-related technical assistance and training and therefore must be made readily and widely available.

Exchanges of information among planners and decision-makers have helped determine the direction of drought-related research, and sharing of findings among research entities has helped promote many of the advances in drought-related research. The Commission heard that there are various opportunities to expand such collaborative and cooperative activities. We also heard that research benefits greatly from trained, skilled people who have a deep and abiding interest in drought-related issues. As technology and knowledge evolve, so does the need for a new generation of trained, skilled, and interested individuals.

Insurance

It is evident from the information we received and assessments we conducted that even the best preparedness and proactive mitigation measures will not adequately address some drought-related risks. Small businesses such as marinas and water-based recreation enterprises, for example, are vulnerable to the impacts of drought. In addition, Main Street enterprises that rely heavily on income from agriculture or water-based recreation businesses suffer when those businesses lose income.

Insurance is one approach that individuals can choose to take on their own. The Small Business Administration noted that business interruption insurance is available in private insurance markets. However, it is generally not tailored to the needs of small businesses in drought situations.

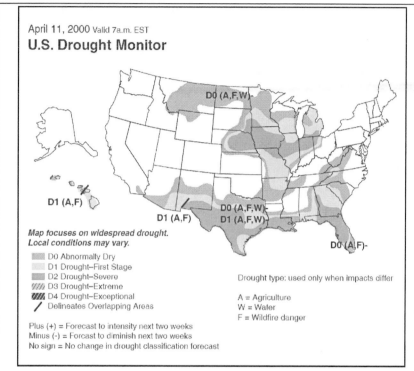

April 11, 2000 Valid 7a.m. EST
U.S. Drought Monitor

D0 (A,F,W)-

D1 (A,F)

D1 (A,F)

D0 (A,F,W)-
D1 (A,F,W)-

D0 (A,F)-

Map focuses on widespread drought.
Local conditions may vary.

- D0 Abnormally Dry
- D1 Drought–First Stage
- D2 Drought–Severe
- D3 Drought–Extreme
- D4 Drought–Exceptional
- Delineates Overlapping Areas

Drought type: used only when impacts differ

A = Agriculture
W = Water
F = Wildfire danger

Plus (+) = Forecast to intensify next two weeks
Minus (-) = Forcast to diminish next two weeks
No sign = No change in drought classification forecast

The U.S. Department of Commerce, U.S. Department of Agriculture, and National Drought Mitigation Center publish a weekly, Drought Monitor on the Internet, posted at http://enso.unl.edu/monitor/monitor. html. The Monitor serves as an excellent example of a collaborative effort to pull together the various sources of weather data and compile them in a single, comprehensive, national report. In addition to the map, the Monitor includes a summary of recent significant weather as well as forecasts of conditions that could affect drought intensities in upcoming weeks.

RESEARCH AT WORK

Our analysis indicates that research has proved essential in several drought-related areas. As examples:

- Research that identified germplasm and dominant genes in naturally occurring drought-tolerant plants has benefitted the production of non-irrigated crops and forages that are totally dependent on rainfall.
- Research has identified characteristics of impacts resulting from changes in weather patterns such as El Niño, La Niña, and the North Atlantic Oscillation.
- Research has provided the technological base needed for long-range weather prediction and the acquisition of improved data on climate and weather phenomena to improve the accuracy of those predictions.
- Research provides information needed by individuals, communities, states, and regions to facilitate more efficient water use. It has been the impetus for numerous technological improvements in irrigation efficiency, desalination, wastewater treatment, and household items such as ultra-low flow toilets and horizontal-axis clothes washers among other technologies. In Florida, more than 100 desalination plants are in operation (*Water International*, December 1999). Communities in California are also using desalination technology, as we learned at our Los Angeles hearing.

Small businesses may also lack access to information about the financial and business management strategies available to them.

Insurance has been a central feature of U.S. agricultural policy for decades. And while farmers and ranchers are also among the first to feel the impacts of drought, the federal crop insurance program, as noted earlier, covers only major field crops, not all vegetable and other crops in all locations or livestock.

A variety of strategies were offered for the Commission's consideration. Some were variations on the crop insurance program but with emphasis on self-help, extended coverage, resource stewardship, and preparedness. Many have been and are being discussed in a variety of forums, including the U.S. Congress. In-depth analysis of these strategies would require much more time and many more resources than were available to the Commission. We therefore endorse none of the approaches but present the following summary.

- One approach called for incorporating all crops and livestock into the crop insurance program and for taking a "whole-farm" approach to insurance. That means losses from one crop or one type of livestock could be offset by gains in a different crop or type of livestock on the same farm.

- Another approach discussed at the Commission's hearings in Austin, Atlanta, and Billings would replace the current crop insurance program with one based on the cost of production. Under this program, all crops and livestock would be included on a whole-farm basis. The federal government would subsidize premiums, but at different rates than under the current program. Payments would be made when income is less than 90% of the documented cost of production. Paid premiums would be maintained in a national trust fund for disbursement.

- A third option was to base crop insurance payments on the same criteria used to make direct payments to farmers for resource conservation measures under the Conservation Security Program proposed in the Administration's 2001 budget. The objective is to recognize stewardship of farm and range lands and water on farms and ranches, which are valuable assets in addition to the crops and livestock raised on those lands.

- In counties of Florida, Michigan, Massachusetts, and several other states where farmers often produce a variety of specialty crops, the Department of Agriculture is testing the Adjusted Gross Revenue model. This insurance plan incorporates the whole-farm approach and uses a farmer's historical Schedule F tax form information as a base to provide guaranteed revenue during the period of insurance coverage. This model provides an insurance safety net for multiple agricultural commodities in one insurance package.

- A different approach stems from the Australian Drought Policy Review Task Force's report issued in 1990. The Task Force's goal was to achieve self-reliance among farmers and recommended that only in extreme circumstances—a one in 20- to 25-year drought event that lasts 12 months—would the government provide aid in the form of debt subsidies and income support. The respective roles for farmers and the government were clearly spelled out. Farmers would assume greater responsibility for managing risks arising from climate variability while the government would help create an overall environment conducive to this planning and risk-management approach. The government would increase funding for drought research and training on drought risk management and provide savings incentives and tax policy changes. The Australian approach does not include provisions for government crop insurance.

Relief

Many comments we received recognized the importance of moving away from the traditional approach to drought that is driven by emergency relief to a new approach that emphasizes planning and proactive mitigation. At the same time, we were cautioned that it will take time to provide the training and technical assistance needed to help farmers, ranchers, local businesses, communities, states, and tribes make this transition. A safety net is needed, we were told, to help overcome the impacts of extreme occurrences of drought or the impacts of multi-faceted disasters (for example, flood/drought or hail/drought).

Approximately 47 federal programs have an element of drought-related relief, primarily for agricultural droughts. The U.S. Department of Agriculture, for example, follows a "bottom up" procedure for emergency disaster designations, but the Commission recognizes that the process needs to be streamlined. In every county in the nation, there is a County Emergency Board consisting of a representative from each of the five Department of Agriculture agencies that normally have offices in the county. A similar structure exists at the state level. When a state governor gets a request for a disaster designation related to agricultural issues, such as drought, the governor asks the Secretary of the Department of Agriculture to designate an administrative disaster. The Secretary sends the request to the national office of the Farm Service Agency. From there, it goes back to the State Emergency Board, which works with the relevant County Emergency Board(s) to analyze the situation and determine whether or not conditions exist for the disaster designation.

The Department of Agriculture also has several ongoing and *ad hoc* programs that provide financial relief to farmers who have suffered drought-related losses. The Emergency Conservation Program, the Emergency Watershed Program, the Non-insured Crop Disaster Assistance Program, and the Federal Crop Insurance Program are examples. These and other emergency relief programs require congressional action and are dependent on the appropriations process or emergency supplemental appropriations. The funding for drought, floods, and economic assistance approached $16 billion over the past two years.

But many agricultural producers expressed concerns about these types of responses. For example, a farmer who testified at the Commission's hearing in Austin experienced a significant drought during the summer of 1999. He finished harvest in August, but the Farm Service Agency could not take his application for assistance until December. By February of 2000, assistance was still not available. During the 1999 drought in the mid-Atlantic and southeastern states, the Department of Agriculture, under the Secretarial disaster designation, could only provide assistance through the Emergency Conservation Program and take loan applications, pending congressional appropriations. Comments from the Agriculture Department note that once appropriations are received, the tens and sometimes hundreds of thousands of applications must then be processed within existing personnel constraints. For these reasons, assistance is often "too little and too late," as we heard time and again at our public hearings.

Public witnesses at the Commission's hearing in Billings said that documentation acceptable to trigger federal response for one Department of Agriculture emergency program was not sufficient to trigger other Department emergency programs. They said that they often fail to get a clear understanding of what additional information is needed to meet program criteria and that this causes confusion for everyone, including the agency staff administering the program. And witnesses at several of the Commission's hearings said that they were frustrated by the Department's Emergency Conservation Program. That program can help them develop emergency livestock watering facilities in times of dire need, but the program seldom provides timely assistance. This may be due in part to the fact that the program is funded by supplemental appropriations from Congress after the fact.

Title I of Public Law 102-250 authorizes the Bureau of Reclamation to provide emergency response assistance, including emergency well drilling. However, Title I is temporary, and the assistance it authorizes is available only within the 17 so-called "Reclamation" states in the West. Title I is the only federal law that authorizes water deliveries "from Federal Reclamation projects and non-project water...on a non-reimbursable basis for the purposes of protecting or restoring fish and wildlife resources." Public Law 102-250 is also the basis for the Bureau's drought planning and education assistance. All of these activities must therefore share the funds for this program.

Public Law 95-51 provides the Secretary of the Army authority under certain conditions to construct wells and transport water to farmers, ranchers, and political subdivisions within areas that the Assistant Secretary of the Army for Civil Works determines to be drought distressed. Any farmer, rancher, or political subdivision within a distressed area may submit a written request for assistance. But Corps assistance is considered only when nonfederal interests have exhausted reasonable means for securing necessary water supplies (within the limits of their financial resources), including assistance from other federal agencies. And Corps assistance is always considered to be supplemental to state and local efforts. For example, Corps assistance is not used to provide drought emergency water where a livestock owner has other options such as loans, selling all or part of a herd even at deflated prices, and relocating animals to an area where water is available. As another example, Corps assistance can be provided to construct wells, but the Corps' costs for construction must be repaid. In addition, Corps assistance can be provided to transport water for consumption. The Corps covers the cost of transporting the water, but the cost of purchasing and storing the water is the nonfederal interest's responsibility. This water-hauling program, which seems to offer assistance at first glance, is actually a program of last resort under the current law, with very restrictive eligibility criteria.

The 1966 Flood Control Act allows the Corps to contract with states, municipalities, private entities, or individuals for surplus water that may be available in any reservoir under the control of the Department of the Army. Withdrawals are for domestic and industrial uses. The preferred approach in providing such surplus water is for a state or subdivision of a state to enter into a contract with the Secretary of the Army and agree to act as wholesaler for all of the water requirements of individual users. This places the state or local government in a position to help their citizens during difficult times and minimizes the potential for problems that could arise if the Secretary of the Army had to determine who is entitled to shares of surplus water based on assessments of local needs. All such withdrawals require a fee for the service provided, even in the case of a declared national disaster area.

The Stafford Act and its implementation by the Federal Emergency Management Agency is an effective, proven model for organizing and providing emergency assistance during most catastrophic natural disasters. One of the factors that makes this program successful is that the Agency can draw monies from an annual appropriated fund to pay for disaster assistance. The Agency can provide disaster unemployment assistance, truck in water, and assist in replacing or building infrastructure such as wells or pipelines for water transfers. The Stafford Act authorizes only measures to protect health and safety, however, and has rarely been used to respond to drought-caused emergencies. In addition, it takes a presidential declaration of disaster before Stafford Act authority can be activated. Not all drought events will be declared disasters at the presidential level, although they may well have adverse impacts.

Need to Coordinate Drought-Related Programs

As shown in much of the preceding discussion, the array of state, federal, and other drought-related programs can be intimidating and frustrating for those who would like access to the services the programs offer, but who do not deal with government agencies on a regular basis. At another level, the multitude of federal programs can also cause problems for state, county, and tribal governments that may be very used to governmental transactions but still have to deal individually with separate federal agencies for any number of drought-related issues.

Service delivery networks exist for many drought-related programs at all levels of government. However, we heard that they are not well integrated, and the people who need information about the programs are not always well served. People told us there is no central point of contact concerning all federal programs and that even within the same federal department, there may be many drought-related programs and no single contact point to advise people about what they may qualify for or how to access the programs. We also heard that the delivery time for assistance in many cases is unsatisfactory, partly because there is little coordination of programs.

The Western Drought Coordination Council strongly suggested establishing a federal drought coordinating body. The law that created this Commission indicated a need to develop an effective coordinated federal approach to drought mitigation and response. The law required us to determine if all federal drought programs should be consolidated under one entity.

In arriving at our recommendations, we considered the consolidation option and concluded it would be impractical and ineffective. Drought affects a wide array of constituents—among them farmers, ranchers, non-farm businesses, tribes, water districts, municipalities, and industry—as well as the environment. The federal expertise required to address the needs of these constituents and the impacts of drought on the environment resides in many agencies. The federal agencies currently involved in drought programs report to multiple congressional authorizing and appropriating committees, making it difficult to restructure these authorities in a timely manner.

We also considered three other options. The first was a National Drought Council similar in composition to the National Drought Policy Commission, but that also includes a representative from the U.S. Department of Energy, a representative from the Environmental Protection Agency, and a nonfederal, nongovernment environmental representative. The second option was a presidentially created federal drought coordination body comprised of only federal representatives from the appropriate federal agencies. This entity would be directed to coordinate with state and local governments, tribes, regional drought-related entities, and the private sector in carrying out its duties. The third option was to build on existing, less formal models such as the Resource Conservation and Development Councils or the Association of State Dam Safety Officials.

In the end, we agreed that coordination would be more effective if nonfederal participation were explicitly established (see Recommendation 5.1).

Need for Public Education

We heard often during our deliberations that a key element in successful drought preparedness is public education. Many people are made aware of the need for water conservation and other measures during drought. But once drought is over, old habits tend to dominate.

Most examples of successful public education campaigns presented during our hearings stemmed from local and state governmental activity or from private and nongovernmental entities. As an example, the California Urban Water Conservation Council identified 14 best management practices, three of which relate to education, public awareness, and communications. One calls for organizations to identify a "water conservation coordinator" as a single contact point for information. Two others call for development and implementation of coordinated public and school education programs. Included in the education programs are work-shops, newsletters, public service announcements, press releases, town hall meetings, school curricula, bill stuffers for utilities, and interactive participatory decision-making processes. These techniques and others provide communication links among organizations that provide assistance and the people whom they serve. Such techniques also help increase awareness of the value of preparedness to reduce costly impacts of droughts.

There is little federal assistance available for such programs, but there are a few examples of federal public education efforts related to drought. One is the National Weather Service's recent addition of drought concerns to its annual spring media briefings on the water supply outlook. For the March 13, 2000, presentation, the Weather Service prepared a public document to emphasize the importance of preparing for drought. In addition, the Weather

Service produced maps to show current drought areas nationwide as well as seasonal drought outlooks and provided a list of drought information sources.

CALIFORNIA URBAN WATER CONSERVATION COUNCIL—14 BEST MANAGEMENT PRACTICES

1. Indoor and outdoor home water use survey.
2. Residential plumbing retrofit (low cost: faucet aerators, shower heads, toilet dams, etc.).
3. Water utility system audits; leak detection and repair.
4. Metering with commodity rates.
5. Large landscape conservation incentives (irrigation meters, etc.).
6. High-efficiency washing machine rebates (horizontal axis).
7. Public information programs.
8. School education programs.
9. Commercial/industrial/institutional water use survey.
10. Wholesale water agency financial/technical assistance to small retail agencies.
11. Conservation pricing—more water used, higher the price.
12. Water Conservation Coordinator.
13. Water waste prohibition (do not allow gutter flooding, non-recycling water fountains, etc.).
14. Residential Ultra-Low Flow Toilet Replacement Program (rebates, installation, etc.).

On another front, the National Disaster Education Coalition, a group of public and private organizations that provides educational materials and information on natural hazards, met in February 2000 to discuss a plan for incorporating drought into its ongoing efforts.

We were cautioned, however, that there is a need to include the media in public education outreach. Widespread but misinformed drought alerts can do damage to state or regional tourism and recreation economies when the actual impacts may be confined to a small portion of the state or region.

Need to Address Environmental Concerns

As many people testified during our hearings or through written comments, drought can have devastating impacts on aquatic and terrestrial environmental resources, as well as on human users of water. Aquatic ecosystems are exceptionally vulnerable to the effects of drought conditions, manifested as reductions in streamflows, and populations of terrestrial wildlife are placed under stress when severe drought conditions develop. Habitat quality and quantity gradually decline from lack of moisture, increasing the competition for limited resources. Wildlife species eventually suffer from lack of drinking water, forage, and cover and from heat stress. We heard that the biotic impacts of drought are particularly acute for threatened, endangered, and sensitive species of fish and wildlife that are characteristically found in low population densities. In many cases, such species have already encountered damage to or destruction of their natural environments because of factors such as suburban sprawl, conversion of land to agricultural or industrial uses, and construction of large dams or other impoundments.

> *Environmental resources often receive inadequate attention during drought emergencies and in drought planning, not so much because of lack of concern but because of lack of expertise in this arena, lack of adequate financial resources, and sometimes lack of awareness.*

We heard that in areas where large quantities of water are stored behind dams, the dams segment rivers and thus impede the movement of fish and change the pattern of sediment deposition. Dams also allow the regulation of river flows, and the preference is generally for moderate flows with no floods and no low flows. Riverine ecosystems that evolved before the dams were built and the life they sustain may be eliminated. The most common examples are anadromous fish that can no longer navigate the river and riverine species whose food cycle depends on the frequent flooding of riverbanks. But dams also eliminate some of the effects of severe droughts, so species that could not survive as well in the natural hydrologic cycle may now prosper. New species, welcome and unwelcome, may be introduced. Reservoirs often support popular game fish that would not have been found in the natural river.

Drought also has repercussions on the morphology and hydrologic function of stream channel networks and on the chemistry and water quality of streams and lakes. On land, it can lead to major episodes of tree mortality, initiate out-breaks of insects and disease in forests, and limit an ecosystem's productivity and ability to cycle essential elements.

Witnesses noted that environmental resources often receive inadequate attention during drought emergencies and in drought planning, not so much because of lack of concern but because of lack of expertise in this arena, lack of adequate financial resources, and sometimes lack of awareness. Drought planners may fail to determine which drought-related environmental impacts can be tolerated and which cannot and therefore would benefit from appropriate drought impact-reduction measures. Larger questions also remain to be answered, including the degree to which humans should try to eliminate the effect of drought on the environment if drought is a natural part of the environmental cycle.

Additional concerns center on use of water for humans and the environment, including ad-equate stream flows for wildlife species, and determination of preferences when one species competes with another for water. Some people suggested that during drought, environmental regulations—ranging from those concerning wildlife and wildlife habitat to those related to safe drinking water—should be more flexible. On the other hand, we heard that droughts are the very times when enforcement of such regulations is essential to protect environmental resources, including drinking water supplies, that are already stressed from factors not related to drought. We heard too that addressing environmental concerns in relation to drought might best be accomplished in the context of ecosystem management and restoration and as part of planning for watersheds or river basins because many of these concerns extend across human-drawn boundaries and borders.

The Commission appreciates the complexities of these issues. As the Western Water Policy Review Advisory Commission stated in its June 1998 report, "Today, there are a number of federal, state, tribal and local agencies with competing interests and missions related to water, but none with a sufficient political or legal mandate to override the concerns of the others. This means that implementing any proposal, for almost any purpose, requires working through a complicated web of laws, regulations, and constituencies." The report cited the CALFED program in the San Francisco Bay-Delta region of California as a model for resolving complex water disputes, noting that the program brought together representatives of agricultural, business, environmental, and urban concerns "to guarantee more reliable water supplies and improved water quality for the environment, cities, and farms."

When drought hits arid farmland or fast-growing urban/suburban regions, it can heighten tensions over water use. This was the topic of lead stories on the March 13, 2000, CBS and ABC prime-time newscasts, which focused on questions about who should get water and for what purpose in the Southeast and drought-stricken Texas. A few days earlier on March 9, the Seattle *Post-Intelligencer* reported on conflicts between the City of Seattle and King County over the county's attempts to involve all municipal jurisdictions in the county—including Seattle— in development of a regional water resources plan that includes considerations for salmon runs.

The Western Governors' Association, the National Governors' Association, and the National Association of Counties have adopted a set of principles to guide their environmental management efforts. Called "Enlibra," the principles form the basis of a shared doctrine that "speaks to greater participation and collaboration in decision making, focuses on outcomes rather than just programs, and recognizes the need for a variety of tools beyond regulation that will improve environmental and natural resource management" (www.westgov.org).

We are encouraged by these and other examples that incorporate a broad array of environmental impacts and concerns into their processes to give interested parties a chance to reduce conflicts. We caution that in relation to drought, some preparedness and proactive mitigation measures may in and of themselves create unacceptable impacts on the environment. For this reason, it is doubly important that environmental resource issues be included in drought preparedness efforts.

Need to Address Drought-Related Wildfires

We heard that drought events often give rise to increased risk of widespread wildfires. In turn, wildfires can exacerbate the environmental impacts of drought by consuming vegetation already stressed from drought, by burning protective streamside vegetation, and in severe-intensity fires by changing soil composition and properties. We were told, too, that in areas where drought occurrences are rare, people are often unprepared for wildfire. Even areas where drought is more common may lack sufficient resources for combating wildfire. Witnesses from Oklahoma and Texas told us during our hearing in Austin that they rely primarily on volunteer fire fighters to control drought-related wildfire and that they are in need of equipment and training to do a better job and help ensure the safety of the fire fighters. In written comments, New Mexico's state forestry division noted that accurate weather predictions are important to fire managers for safety reasons. The comments also said that the Palmer Drought Index, with its emphasis on soil moisture, is not sufficient to give fire managers the information they need about fuel moisture, a statement that was echoed in other comments we received.

A 1996 report of the Western Governors' Association identified three major obstacles in suppression of drought-related wildfires:

- the financial burdens to prepare for and fight the fires,
- a lack of proper training and resources, and
- restoring forest and grassland health.

Wildfire risks may well increase with drought—along the suburban/ rural interface as well as on wildlands.

The U.S. Department of Agriculture Forest Service is authorized by the Cooperative Forestry Assistance Act of 1978 to cooperate with states in developing systems and methods for prevention, control, suppression, and prescribed use of fires in rural areas. The goal is to protect human lives, agricultural crops and livestock, property and other improvements, and natural resources. The Forest Service's Fire Sciences Laboratory has developed many tools to address fire danger and fire behavior potential at national and local levels. One tool to display broad-scale elements of fire danger is the Wildland Fire Assessment System, which is available on the Internet.

The Federal Emergency Management Agency emphasized that wildfire is part of the wildland/urban interface—no longer a phenomenon concentrated primarily in large national forests and parks or on vast expanses of agricultural land. The Agency noted that the number of requests it received from states for assistance with wildfire increased from an average of five to seven a year during most of the 1980s to 122 in 1998.

We learned also that the Resource Conservation and Development Councils across the country are encouraging and assisting in the installation of "dry hydrants." These relatively inexpensive structures allow fire trucks to load water from ponds on cooperating farms during emergencies.

Need for Training and Technical Assistance

Planning provides opportunities for the general public to become involved and invested in drought-related decisions—for example, adopting water conservation measures year round. Planning also gives people a chance to learn more about drought, leading to greater self-reliance and self-determination. And planning emphasizes local solutions based on consideration of all affected entities and related issues, including legal, economic, geographic, climate, religious, and cultural differences; fairness and equity; and environmental concerns. These opportunities are lost where people are not sufficiently trained to engage in drought planning or lack adequate technical assistance to do so.

Hands-on training and technical assistance programs can help people formulate and implement plans to mitigate human and environmental impacts. Such programs can help farmers decide whether to include drought-resistant crops, on-farm wells, crop insurance, conservation systems, restoration of wetlands and wildlife habitat, and other important factors into their risk-management strategies. They can help farmers install water management practices and gain a basic understanding of the soils and climate conditions in their areas and the types of crops and plants suitable to those sometimes changing conditions. Such assistance can also help them understand complicated marketing options and other methods to manage risks.

Training and technical assistance programs can help communities as they determine their own priorities for incorporating drought concerns and the need to protect environmental resources into ongoing community planning and comprehensive water management plans aimed at ensuring safe, adequate drinking water (urban and rural) as well as water needed to fight fires. They can help drought planners decide whether they would benefit from simulated drought-response exercises like those conducted by the Army Corps of Engineers.

We often heard that local governments know their situations related to impending drought better than anyone else. We were told that cooperation and assistance from states and the federal government through incentives, funding, and technical assistance in drought planning would go far to help small communities and rural water systems prepare better for drought. We learned that technical assistance and training would be helpful as people gather drought-related information, devise drought impact-reduction strategies, and prepare public education and involvement campaigns to develop locally appropriate solutions. State climatologists and researchers in university drought-related programs, as well as federal experts, are potential sources for training assistance. In addition, federal and state agencies often have had experience with the types of emergencies that can occur and what measures were taken to respond to the emergencies. Examples of such measures are standard operating procedures for laying emergency pipelines, trucking water, or identifying ponds in the areas where fire fighters can obtain water to fight wildfires.

Experts and members of the public also advised us that we should make greater use of innovative water supply techniques. We saw practical applications such as the Scottsdale system for treating wastewater and injecting it into the ground for later use. But we were unable to find an authoritative guide that documents the arguments for and against the full range of "water-creating" methods such as desalination and cloud seeding. Without such information, it is less likely that water managers will fully consider these options. Even if the managers want to learn more, they are on their own to study the literature, which currently includes a great deal about water-making methods but little about the costs and impacts of these methods.

Need to Address International Drought-Related Issues

Because drought is a worldwide phenomenon, the United States has the opportunity to share drought experience and expertise with other countries and to learn from them. We heard from federal agency personnel that several information-sharing projects are underway through the United Nations and other entities. In the arena of water supplies, the border between the U.S. and Canada cuts across natural drainage basins. Thus, the actions of one country can affect the other, and the impacts of drought can cross the border. Although drought is a serious issue in the Columbia River and Great Lakes basins, the two countries have strong working relationships on these issues. For example, droughts can lower the levels of the Great Lakes and thereby reduce hydropower generation, increase shipping costs, and make the lakes less accessible to recreational boaters. The primary response is to dredge more and to extend boat ramps. The International Boundary and Water Commission monitors allocation of water from the Colorado and Rio Grande rivers between the United States and Mexico. We heard that Mexico currently owes the United States water from the Rio Grande, but has not provided it. We also heard from witnesses during our hearings in El Paso and Austin that this has had negative impacts on the drought-stricken lower Rio Grande section of Texas. The witnesses told us that there is a need for watershed planning of the entire river basin, which is located in both the United States and Mexico.

CONCLUSION

From the preceding findings, we drew the following conclusions:

- The United States would benefit from development of national drought policy with preparedness as its core.
- Preparedness measures, particularly comprehensive drought planning and proactive mitigation measures, can lessen the impact of drought on individuals, communities, and the environment. They can also reduce the need for future emergency financial and other relief.
- Effective drought plans should have clearly identified objectives and performance standards and a clear exposition of the vulnerability of a region to drought, given current and expected water resources infrastructure and water uses. They should be flexible to avoid a "one size fits all" approach and allow for social, cultural, and religious differences. For both urban and rural communities, they should consider the location of alternate or supplemental sources of water, how this water can be conveyed to the point of need, and whether additional treatment is needed. They should also be based on cost and performance.

- Effective plans should evaluate drought programs to determine whether they identify and address priority environmental impacts and improve proactive mitigation of drought's impacts on the environment through training, incentives, technical assistance, research, and public education. Effective plans should consider the allocation of water to meet the need to protect the environment and to meet immediate human needs.

- The people and entities that are likely to receive the greatest share of federal emergency assistance because of drought often have the fewest personnel, information, and financial resources to prepare for and reduce the potential impacts of drought.

- Individuals, businesses, local/county/state governments, tribes, and nongovernmental organizations with an interest in or responsibilities for drought management would benefit from training and technical assistance to plan for and reduce the impacts of drought.

- There are a number of success stories in drought preparedness and proactive mitigation at the individual, local, state, regional, and federal levels that would make excellent models for use in training and technical assistance. Among those cited in this chapter are the nonprofit TreePeople's "Second Nature" program in Los Angeles, the Metropolitan Water District of Southern California's "Integrated Resource" and "Water Surplus and Demand Management" plans, Kentucky's drought management plan, the Georgia Water Management Campaign, the U.S. Bureau of Reclamation's Drought Program, the Army Corps of Engineers' simulated drought exercises, and the small water-sheds assistance offered by the U.S. Department of Agriculture

- Partnerships among nonfederal governments, the federal government, and private interests can go far in developing the tools and strategies for formulating and carrying out appropriate drought preparedness strategies.

- Proactive mitigation activities such as water conservation, science-based forest management, reuse of wastewater, desalination, pricing strategies, and the identification of back-up water supplies—when initiated before an emergency—can reduce vulnerability to drought events.

- In some parts of the country, there is insufficient area coverage or recorded history for stream gage and climate data.

- Drought-related data can be better marshaled, interpreted, and disseminated to all parties with an interest in drought, including the media and public at large, so that citizens and experts in drought management alike can gain the knowledge they need to help lessen the impacts of drought.

- Drought-related research is the foundation of many drought programs and is critical in the production of high-quality innovations and technology that lead to improved drought preparedness.

- Even the best preparedness measures may not sufficiently reduce many risks associated with drought nor eliminate the need for emergency relief during severe droughts.

- There is considerable sentiment among farmers, ranchers, and tribes to make the U.S. Department of Agriculture's crop insurance more responsive to their needs by extending coverage to include all crops and livestock.

- Disaster declarations are much less common for severe urban droughts than for agricultural droughts. Like agricultural droughts, however, they will occur despite the best preparedness measures.

- Federal drought-related programs lack a coordinated approach so that delivery of program services is less efficient, effective, and timely than it could be. The U.S. Department of Agriculture and other federal agencies involved in assisting people with drought activities need to improve their internal and external coordination practices to provide services more appropriately and expediently.

- Some federal drought-related programs are neither authorized nor funded at the level needed to deliver effective services. Furthermore, their eligibility criteria and cost-sharing requirements may restrict participation by tribes, farmers and ranchers, and others who may have limited resources.

RECOMMENDATIONS

Policy Statement

The Commission believes that national drought policy should use the resources of the federal government to support but not supplant nor interfere with state, tribal, regional, local, and individual efforts to reduce drought impacts. The guiding principles of national drought policy should be:

- Favor preparedness over insurance, insurance over relief, and incentives over regulation.
- Set research priorities based on the potential of the research results to reduce drought impacts.
- Coordinate the delivery of federal services through cooperation and collaboration with nonfederal entities.

This policy requires a shift from the current emphasis on drought relief. It means we must adopt a forward-looking stance to reduce this nation's vulnerability to the impacts of drought. Preparedness—especially drought planning, plan implementation, and proactive mitigation—must become the cornerstone of national drought policy. This basic concept was the conclusion reached by the Senate Task Force on Funding Disaster Relief in March 1995, among other entities. It was universally supported within the Commission and by the overwhelming majority of people who commented on the draft version of this chapter. We recommend that Congress pass a National Drought Preparedness Act, which would establish a nonfederal/federal partnership through a National Drought Council as described in Recommendation 5.1. The primary function of the Council is to ensure that the goals of national drought policy are achieved. The goals are:

1. Incorporate planning, implementation of plans and proactive mitigation measures, risk management, resource stewardship, environmental considerations, and public education as the key elements of effective national drought policy.
2. Improve collaboration among scientists and managers to enhance the effectiveness of observation networks, monitoring, prediction, information delivery, and applied research and to foster public understanding of and preparedness for drought.
3. Develop and incorporate comprehensive insurance and financial strategies into drought preparedness plans.
4. Maintain a safety net of emergency relief that emphasizes sound stewardship of natural resources and self-help.
5. Coordinate drought programs and response effectively, efficiently, and in a customer-oriented manner.

Goal 1

Incorporate planning, implementation of plans and proactive mitigation measures, risk management, resource stewardship, environmental considerations, and public education as the key elements of effective national drought policy.

In accordance with the law that established the National Drought Policy Commission, we strongly endorse preparedness as a key element to reduce the impacts of drought on individuals, communities, and the environment. We heard convincing testimony and reviewed expert analyses that led us to conclude most levels of government and most of the private sector are not adequately prepared for drought. We believe that coordinated drought preparedness programs will lessen the need for future emergency financial and other assistance. Basic components of preparedness include long-term planning, implementation of proactive mitigation measures, risk management, resource stewardship, environmental considerations, and public education.

Specific Recommendations

1.1 Congress should adequately fund existing drought preparedness programs such as the U.S. Department of Agriculture's Conservation Technical Assistance Program (Public Law 46) and Environmental Quality Incentives Program (16 U.S.C. 3839) and the Bureau of Reclamation's drought planning program (Public Law 102-250, Title II).

1.2 The President should direct the Bureau of Reclamation and the Army Corps of Engineers to find an effective way to meet the drought planning needs of those areas not traditionally served by the Bureau of Reclamation. Congress should fund these agencies' efforts to better serve the needs of the eastern part of the country.

1.3 The President should direct all appropriate federal agencies to cooperate fully and to provide all assistance possible to encourage development or revision and implementation of comprehensive drought preparedness plans by states, localities, tribes, regional entities such as watershed and river basin organizations, and the private sector. Federal agencies that provide drought planning assistance should consider the elements shown in the box below.

1.4 Federal agencies providing drought planning assistance should encourage state, local, regional and tribal planners to use or adapt existing planning materials and resources. These include materials developed by the National Drought Mitigation Center, the Army Corps of Engineers, the U.S. Department of Agriculture, the Western Drought Coordination Council, the states, and urban and rural water districts.

1.5 The President should direct all appropriate federal agencies to develop and implement drought management plans for federal facilities such as military bases, federal prisons, and large federal office complexes in the United States. These plans should be coordinated with local and state drought planning and mitigation measures.

1.6 The President should direct all appropriate federal agencies to study their programs for potential impacts on drought. Where such potential exists, the agencies need to integrate national drought policy into their programs.

1.7 The President should direct federal agencies with water resources management programs to develop and promote comprehensive public awareness efforts as part of an ongoing drought preparedness strategy.

COMMON COMPONENTS OF COMPREHENSIVE WATER MANAGEMENT/DROUGHT PLANNING

- Analysis of past, current and projected water demand, instream flow needs for appropriate ecosystem protection, water availability, and (from these) potential water shortages.
- The basis for the design and performance of the plan, including the economic, environmental, social, and cultural goals and objectives of decision makers and the public at large and performance metrics derived from those objectives.
- Description of how shortages would be met (for example, planting of drought-resistant species, temporary fallowing of land, increased supply, leak detection/elimination, water use efficiency, demand management) and an estimate of associated costs.
- Description of interagency/intergovernmental coordination and public participation.
- Appropriate mitigation of drought impacts on the environment.
- Monitoring and prediction strategies.

- Methods for testing the plans.
- Mechanisms for updating the plans.
- A decision-making body to oversee and implement the plans.

The Commission encourages drought planning as a continuing process and part of more comprehensive water management programs.

SAMPLE PUBLIC AWARENESS ACTIVITIES

- Public involvement before, during, and after the development of drought preparedness plans: The planning entity should seek broad community input and support for the planning effort. Participation should be actively solicited from a full spectrum of the local population—all age groups, all cultural and ethnic groups, and all economic levels.
- Public information: The public needs to have access to understandable, informative materials on all aspects of drought. Examples of such materials include: explanations of the causes of drought, its impacts, and the damage it causes; descriptions of the value and benefits of sound land stewardship to reduce the impacts of drought and protect the environment; clear instructions for appropriate responses to drought (water conservation, water reuse, and leak detection/elimination among others); and requirements of local ordinances or state law during droughts. This information should be provided in as many locations and as many formats as possible, including printed booklets or brochures, telephone hotlines, public service announcements, media events, computer web pages, and classroom presentations.

Goal 2

Improve collaboration among scientists and managers to enhance the effectiveness of observation networks, monitoring, prediction, information delivery, and applied research and to foster public understanding of and preparedness for drought.

Our findings and conclusions point out the value of observation networks, monitoring, prediction, information gateways and delivery, and research to drought preparedness. The National Drought Council (see Recommendation 5.1) will coordinate a formal process—such as a drought data monitoring, prediction, and research "summit" of multi-disciplinary, geographically diverse representatives—to ascertain the needs and expectations of all interested parties as a first step toward prioritizing recommendations. Research priorities should address the impacts of drought on non-irrigated systems, aquatic ecosystems, wildlife, and other aspects of the natural environment, including the potential negative impacts of drought mitigation measures. Better coordination of governments and private entities in international drought monitoring, prediction, research, education, water conservation, and technology transfer is essential. The National Drought Council's annual reports will include a description of the information products most needed to reduce drought impacts (see Recommendation 5.4).

> *Better coordination of governments and private entities in international drought monitoring, prediction, research, education, water conservation, and technology transfer is essential.*

Specific Recommendations

2.1 The President should appropriately direct and Congress, as necessary, should authorize and fund a viable plan to maintain, modernize, expand, and coordinate a system of observation networks that meets the needs of the public at large. The plan should include cooperation with states, development and improvement of baseline historical data sets, and recognition of the recommendations made by the National Drought Council. Priority should be placed on filling the gaps on tribal lands and in rural America. Examples of critical observation networks are in the box on the next page.

EXAMPLES OF CRITICAL OBSERVATION NETWORKS

- Department of Commerce, National Weather Service, Cooperative Observer (COOP) Program Hydrometeorological Network
- U.S. Department of Agriculture, Soil Climate Analysis (SCAN) and Snowpack Telemetry (SNOTEL) networks

- U.S. Forest Service, Remote AutomatedWeather Station (RAWS) Network
- U.S. Geological Survey, Streamgaging and Groundwater Network
- Other regional observation networks

2.2 The President should appropriately direct and Congress, as necessary, should authorize and fund continuation of the U.S. Drought Monitor and exploration of opportunities for its improvement and expansion.

2.3 The President should appropriately direct and Congress, as necessary, should authorize and fund continuation of Drought Predictions/Outlooks and development of techniques to improve their accuracy and frequency.

2.4 The President should appropriately direct and Congress, as necessary, should authorize and fund a comprehensive information gateway (possibly through expansion of the National Drought Mitigation Center's website or other similar approaches) to provide users with free and open access to observational network data and drought monitoring, prediction, impact, assessment, preparedness, and mitigation measures. Links among federal and nonfederal sources are critical.

2.5 The President should direct the appropriate federal agencies to develop an effective drought information delivery system such as the Unified Climate Access Network (UCAN) to communicate drought conditions and impacts to decision makers at the federal, regional, state, tribal, and local levels and to the private sector and general public. The systems should include near real-time data, information and products developed at each of these levels and integrated in an appropriate fashion to accurately reflect regional and state differences in drought conditions. The box below indicates some of the critical participants in such a delivery system.

SELECTED CRITICAL PARTICIPANTS IN AN EFFECTIVE DROUGHT INFORMATION DELIVERY SYSTEM

- Climate Prediction Center
- National Climatic Data Center
- Regional Climate Centers
- U.S. Department of Agriculture

- U.S. Geological Survey
- National Drought Mitigation Center
- State Climatologists
- Other regional climate centers
- Other water systems
- International partners

    2.6 The President should direct appropriate federal agencies to expand technology transfer of water conservation strategies and innovative water supply techniques as part of drought preparedness programs.

    2.7 The President should direct and Congress should continue to adequately fund existing and future drought-related research. Existing competitive research grant programs should give high priority to drought. Areas of research should include topics that will either conserve water or make more water available for needs during drought. Examples include alternative methods such as brush control, cloud seeding, canal lining, and desalination.

    2.8 The President should direct and Congress should fund completion of the soil survey on all lands, with special and immediate emphasis on tribal lands.

Goal 3

Develop and incorporate comprehensive insurance and financial strategies into drought preparedness plans.

We firmly believe that preparedness measures will go far to reduce this country's vulnerability to drought.

But we also recognize that prolonged drought causes risks that the best preparedness measures may not adequately address. The most significant approach to such risks in recent years is the federal government's crop insurance program for farmers.

As we heard, however, that program does not cover all crops nor does it cover livestock.

In addition, payments from the program are often "too little, too late" and are administered differently across the country. There is no similar program for others who are at particular risk from drought. Assistance must be pieced together from various sources or is simply not available. Time and again, the federal government is asked to appropriate emergency relief that costs at least $500 million a year on average.

We had neither the expertise nor the resources to investigate thoroughly the various options to improve the crop insurance program or the other proposals that were presented during our deliberations and that Congress has grappled with for many years.

Still, we are convinced that sound insurance and financial strategies are essential if the country is to move away from relying on emergency relief in response to widespread drought.

Specific Recommendations

3.1 We recommend that Congress authorize and fund the U.S. Department of Agriculture to evaluate different approaches to crop insurance, including a cost of production plan. The evaluation should assess whether the approaches are practicable and prudent for all farmers, ranchers, and other stakeholders in all regions of the country and whether they set standards that encourage efficient water use.

3.2 We recommend that the U.S. Department of Agriculture, in cooperation with state and local governments and the private sector, expand training to rural communities, farmers, and ranchers across the country on various financial strategies.

3.3 We recommend that the Small Business Administration, through its private-sector partners, provide information and training to small business owners on developing financial and business management strategies.

During a drought, the incidence of soil erosion may increase.

Goal 4

Maintain a safety net of emergency relief that emphasizes sound stewardship of natural resources and self-help.

The Commission recognizes that over time, efforts at drought preparedness, including risk management, can greatly reduce, but not eliminate, drought-related emergencies. Response measures for drought emergencies can also be useful to respond to water shortages not caused by drought. In all cases where emergency response is required, it should be effective and timely.

Specific Recommendations

4.1 Congress should authorize the Secretary of Agriculture to borrow from the Commodity Credit Corporation to implement the Department of Agriculture's emergency programs.

4.2 Congress should amend the appropriate U.S. Department of Agriculture's emergency programs to include livestock needs during drought.

4.3 The Department of Agriculture should establish a single procedure to trigger, in a timely fashion, all of the Department's disaster programs.

4.4 We recommend that emergency assistance acknowledge, encourage, and reward natural resource stewardship and self-help without discriminating against those truly in need.

4.5 We recommend that Congress enact permanent authorization for Title 1 of Public Law 102-250, which gives the Bureau of Reclamation authority to provide emergency drought assistance. Because the Bureau's authority is limited to the Reclamation states, Congress should extend that authority or provide appropriate authority to the Army Corps of Engineers to serve the non-Reclamation states.

4.6 For those areas not covered by the Stafford Act, Congress should appropriate an annual fund, available until expended and similar to that available under the Stafford Act, for non-farm drought emergencies that affect tribes, communities, businesses, and the environment.

Goal 5

Coordinate drought programs and response effectively, efficiently, and in a customer-oriented manner.

Federal drought programs are a collection of initiatives run by different departments and agencies. Every analysis of past responses to major droughts notes that these programs need to be better coordinated and integrated. We strongly agree. In accordance with our policy statement, we emphasize that coordination of federal drought programs should ensure effective service delivery in support of nonfederal drought programs.

> *Federal drought programs are a collection of initiatives run by different departments and agencies. Every analysis of past responses to major droughts notes that these programs need to be better coordinated and integrated.*

Specific Recommendations

5.1 **Create Council.** The President should immediately establish an interim National Drought Council through an executive order and in combination with a Memorandum of Understanding that provides adequate staffing and funding. Congress should create a long-term, continuing National Drought Council. Both should be composed of federal and regionally diverse nonfederal members (see the table on the next page 40 National Drought Policy Commission Report concerning membership and the designation process). The goal is to implement the recommendations of this chapter as soon as practicable.

5.2 **Co-chairs.** The President should appoint the Secretary of Agriculture as co-chair of the interim National Drought Council, with a nonfederal co-chair elected by the nonfederal interim Council members. Congress should designate the Secretary of Agriculture as the permanent federal co-chair of the long-term Council, with a nonfederal co-chair elected by the nonfederal Council members.

5.3 **Funding.** The President should request and Congress should provide administrative funding to support the interim and long-term National Drought Councils.

5.4 **Duties and process.** The interim and long-term National Drought Councils will be responsible for coordinating the following:

- Timely and efficient delivery of existing federal drought programs.
- Cooperation and participation among federal, state, local, and tribal interests and private water systems in federal drought assistance opportunities by example and through facilitation.
- Program assessments of drought-related assistance efforts.
- Determination of which regions have the most pressing need and greatest opportunities to coordinate and implement drought preparedness assistance programs, recognizing the special drought preparedness needs of tribes, small rural water districts, and small self-supplied water users.

Table. Council membership and designation process

Federal entity	Council member designated by:	Nonfederal representation	Council member designated by:
Department of Agriculture	Department Secretary	East/West Governors	National Governors' Association
Department of the Interior	Department Secretary	County official	National Association of Counties
Federal entity	**Council member designated by:**	**Nonfederal representation**	**Council member designated by:**
Department of Commerce	Department Secretary	City official	U.S. Conference of Mayors
Department of Energy	Department Secretary	Emergency management official	National Emergency Management Association
Department of the Army	Department Secretary	Business	U.S. Chamber of Commerce
Environmental Protection Agency	Agency head	Urban water* Rural water* Tribal*	* Designated by the Secretary of Agriculture

Small Business Administration	Agency head	Environmental* Farm credit*	based on nominations from relevant broad-based groups.
Federal Emergency Management Agency	Agency head	Agricultural producers*	

- Development of an array of coordination strategies to provide support for state, local, and tribal drought planning and mitigation measures.
- Support of state, local, and tribal initiatives to coordinate with current regional drought planning entities, perhaps within watersheds or river basins, or to establish new regional entities.
- An assessment of major river basin initiatives and state programs to determine which methods have proven most effective in reducing conflicts over water.
- Development of a handbook of emergency drought preparedness measures.
- A survey of user groups to ascertain drought monitoring, prediction, and research needs and expectations.
- Establishment of drought impact assessment teams of federal, state, and other experts who are responsible, after drought events occur, for analyzing the causes and aggravating factors that contribute to drought and its social, economic, and environmental impacts.
- Development of a handbook on water supply techniques, including traditional and non-traditional strategies.
- Advocacy of drought-related educational training programs within universities, agencies, and public sector programs.

The co-chairs should report to the President and Congress annually on the progress of these activities

5.5 **Authorization and appropriations.** We recommend that Congress provide federal departments and agencies with appropriate authority and funding needed to carry out the recommendations in this chapter. As noted at the beginning of this chapter, consideration should be given to the costs and benefits associated with drought preparedness, mitigation, and response measures. 42 National Drought Policy Commission Report

APPENDIX A. NATIONAL DROUGHT POLICY ACT

Public Law 105-199

An Act

105th Congress

July 16, 1998
- [H.R. 3035]
note

To establish an advisory commission to provide advice and recommendations on the creation of an integrated, coordinated Federal policy designed to prepare for and respond to serious drought emergencies.

Be it enacted by the Senate and House of Representatives of the United States of America in Congress assembled,

National Drought Policy Act of 1998. note 42 USC 5121 note

SECTION 1. SHORT TITLE.

This Act may be cited as the ``National Drought Policy Act of 1998''.

SEC. 2. FINDINGS.

42 USC 5121 note

Congress finds that—

(1) the United States often suffers serious economic and environmental losses from severe regional droughts and there is no coordinated Federal strategy to respond to such emergencies;

(2) at the Federal level, even though historically there have been frequent, significant droughts of national consequences, drought is addressed mainly through special legislation and ad hoc action rather than through a systematic and permanent process as occurs with other natural disasters;

(3) there is an increasing need, particularly at the Federal level, to emphasize preparedness, mitigation, and risk management (rather than simply crisis management) when addressing drought and other natural disasters or emergencies;

(4) several Federal agencies have a role in drought from predicting, forecasting, and monitoring of drought conditions to the provision of planning, technical, and financial assistance;

(5) there is no single Federal agency in a lead or
coordinating role with regard to drought;

(6) State, local, and tribal governments have had to deal
individually and separately with each Federal agency
involved in drought assistance; and

(7) the President should appoint an advisory commission to
provide advice and recommendations on the creation of
an integrated, coordinated Federal policy designed to
prepare for, mitigate the impacts of, respond to, and
recover from serious drought emergencies.

SEC. 3. ESTABLISHMENT OF COMMISSION.   *42 USC 5121*

(a) Establishment.--There is established a commission to be   *note*
known as the National Drought Policy Commission
(hereafter in this Act referred to as the "Commission").

(b) Membership.—

(1) Composition.--The Commission shall be composed of
16 members. The members of the Commission shall
include—

(A) the Secretary of Agriculture, or the designee of the
Secretary, who shall chair the Commission;

(B) the Secretary of the Interior, or the designee of the
Secretary;

(C) the Secretary of the Army, or the designee of the
Secretary;

(D) the Secretary of Commerce, or the designee of the
Secretary;

(E) the Director of the Federal Emergency Management
Agency, or the designee of the Director;

(F) the Administrator of the Small Business
Administration, or the designee of the Administrator;

(G) two persons nominated by the National Governors'   *President*
Association and appointed by the President, of
whom—
one shall be the governor of a State east of the
Mississippi River; and(ii) one shall be a governor of a
State west of the Mississippi River;

(H) a person nominated by the National Association of *President*
Counties and appointed by the President;
(I) a person nominated by the United States Conference *President*
of Mayors and appointed by the President; and
(J) six persons, appointed by the Secretary of
Agriculture in coordination with the Secretary of the
Interior and the Secretary of the Army, who shall be
representative of groups acutely affected by drought
emergencies, such as the agricultural production
community, the credit community, rural and urban
water associations, Native Americans, and fishing and
environmental interests.
(2) Date.--The appointments of the members of the *Deadline.*
Commission shall be made no later than 60 days after
the date of the enactment of this Act.
(c) Period of Appointment; Vacancies.--Members shall be
appointed for the life of the Commission. Any vacancy in

the Commission shall not affect its powers, but shall be
filled in the same manner as the original appointment.
(d) Initial Meeting.--No later than 30 days after the date on *Deadline.*
which all members of the Commission have been
appointed, the Commission shall hold its first meeting.
(e) Meetings.--The Commission shall meet at the call of the
chair.
(f) Quorum.--A majority of the members of the
Commission shall constitute a quorum, but a lesser
number of members may hold hearings.
(g) Vice Chair.--The Commission shall select a vice chair
from among the members who are not Federal officers or
employees.

SEC. 4. DUTIES OF THE COMMISSION.
(a) Study and Report.--The Commission shall conduct a
thorough study and submit a report on national drought
policy in accordance with this section.
(b) Content of Study and Report.--In conducting the study
and report, the Commission shall--
(1) determine, in consultation with the National Drought

Mitigation Center in Lincoln, Nebraska, and other appropriate entities, what needs exist on the Federal, State, local, and tribal levels to prepare for and respond to drought emergencies;

(2) review all existing Federal laws and programs relating to drought;

(3) review State, local, and tribal laws and programs relating to drought that the Commission finds pertinent;

(4) determine what differences exist between the needs of those affected by drought and the Federal laws and programs designed to mitigate the impacts of and respond to drought;

(5) collaborate with the Western Drought Coordination Council and other appropriate entities in order to consider regional drought initiatives and the application of such initiatives at the national level;

(6) make recommendations on how Federal drought laws and programs can be better integrated with ongoing State, local, and tribal programs into a comprehensive national policy to mitigate the impacts of and respond to drought emergencies without diminishing the rights of States to control water through State law and considering the need for protection of the environment;

(7) make recommendations on improving public awareness of the need for drought mitigation, and prevention; and response on developing a coordinated approach to drought mitigation, prevention, and response by governmental and nongovernmental entities, including academic, private, and nonprofit interests; and

(8) include a recommendation on whether all Federal drought preparation and response programs should be consolidated under one existing Federal agency and, if so, identify such agency.

(c) Submission of Report.--

(1) In general.--No later than 18 months after the date of the enactment of this Act, the Commission shall submit a report to the President and Congress which shall contain a detailed statement of the findings and

Deadline.

conclusions of the Commission, together with its recommendations for such legislation and administrative actions as it considers appropriate.

(2) Approval of report.--Before submission of the report, the contents of the report shall be approved by unanimous consent or majority vote. If the report is approved by majority vote, members voting not to approve the contents shall be given the opportunity to submit dissenting views with the report.

SEC. 5. POWERS OF THE COMMISSION.

42 USC 5121 note.

(a) Hearings.--The Commission may hold such hearings, sit and act at such times and places, take such testimony, and receive such evidence as the Commission considers necessary to carry out the purposes of this Act.

(b) Information From Federal Agencies.--The Commission may secure directly from any Federal department or agency such information as the Commission considers necessary to carry out the provisions of this Act. Upon request of the chair of the Commission, the head of such department or agency shall furnish such information to the Commission.

(c) Postal Services.--The Commission may use the United States mails in the same manner and under the same conditions as other departments and agencies of the Federal Government.

(d) Gifts.--The Commission may accept, use, and dispose of gifts or donations of services or property.

SEC. 6. COMMISSION PERSONNEL MATTERS.

42 USC 5121 note.

(a) Compensation of Members.--Each member of the Commission who is not an officer or employee of the Federal Government shall not be compensated for service on the Commission, except as provided under subsection (b). All members of the Commission who are officers or employees of the United States shall serve without compensation in addition to that received for their services as officers or employees of the United States.

(b) Travel Expenses.--The members of the Commission

shall be allowed travel expenses, including per diem in
lieu of subsistence, at rates authorized for employees of
agencies under subchapter I of chapter 57 of title 5,
United States Code, while away from their homes or
regular places of business in the performance of services
for the Commission.

(c) Detail of Government Employees.--Any Federal
Government employee may be detailed to the
Commission without reimbursement, and such detail
shall be without interruption or loss of civil service status
or privilege.

(d) Administrative Support.--The Secretary of Agriculture
shall provide all financial, administrative, and staff
support services for the Commission.

SEC. 7. TERMINATION OF THE COMMISSION.

*42 USC 5121
note.*

The Commission shall terminate 90 days after the date on
which the Commission submits its report under section 4.
Approved July 16, 1998.
LEGISLATIVE HISTORY--H.R. 3035 (S. 222):
HOUSE REPORTS: No. 105-554, Pt. 1 (Comm. on
Transportation and Infrastructure).
SENATE REPORTS: No. 105-144 accompanying S. 222
(Comm. on Governmental Affairs).
CONGRESSIONAL RECORD, Vol. 144 (1998):
June 16, considered and passed House.
June 24, considered and passed Senate.

INDEX